Positive Dyslexia

by

Roderick I. Nicolson

2015 Edition

Published by Rodin Books, Sheffield, UK

Printed by CreateSpace, an Amazon.com Company

All feedback welcome at   RodNicolson@mac.com

About the Author and the Book

As author and publisher, I feel I ought to write this in the first person!

I am a Professor of Psychology at the University of Sheffield. I have published over 100 academic articles, books or psychological tests, mostly on dyslexia, but also covering education, neuroscience and work psychology.

For the past 25 years I have been a leading UK dyslexia researcher. I co-authored with Angela Fawcett three of the major theories of the cause of dyslexia, and three leading screening tests for dyslexia. I am a passionate and coherent speaker (and was told that I should consider the stage rather than academia). I was nominated for Heretic of the Year in 1996. I am still trying to make a difference.

I first presented the idea of 'Positive Dyslexia' at a British Dyslexia Conference in Liverpool in 2010, and the idea of working to one's strengths rather than one's weaknesses grabbed the attention and enthusiasm of the delegates, leading to many positive suggestions.

The real start of the Positive Dyslexia Initiative was in November 2012 at the International Dyslexia Association Conference in Baltimore, Maryland in the USA. I had the privilege of presenting the initiative to the Parents Conference, with co-presenters my good friends Thomas West and Brock Eide. The symposium generated enormous interest and enthusiasm, with major discussions continuing through Brock and Fernette Eide's Dyslexic Advantage website.

At the conference I presented a blueprint for the 'Positive Dyslexia Journey' from assessment of strengths (not weaknesses) right through Succeeding at School, Succeeding in Work to Succeeding in Society. This book represents the progress we have made since then.

There's still everything to be done, but I think this sets us out on the right track.

A major theme of Positive Dyslexia is 'work to your strengths', and reading certainly is NOT a strength for dyslexia! I have therefore tried to make this book as dyslexia-friendly as possible. Dyslexic adults have strengths in processing visual information, following a narrative, and seeing the big picture. I therefore recorded it as a series of talks, trying to provide a strong narrative. I then transcribed the audio, and then put the figures with the words to give a visually rich format to highlight both the key points and the structure. That's why each page has at least one figure in addition to the text. I think this is actually better for most readers because it gives a choice of reading methods.

'Positive Dyslexia' is also available as a 'ShowBook' in the Apple ibooks format, with the audio-visuals for each slide also available.

This book provides unrivalled ease of reading, with the figures providing an 'at a glance' visual record that makes it much easier to find specific figures, and also to skim rapidly through to the part you are reading. Unlike my 'ShowBook', the book has the advantage of being a physical object that can 'play' by itself!

Acknowledgments

My personal acknowledgments are to my wife, Margaret and our four children, Kate, James, Ben and Ellen who have had to put up with my frequent mental absences while I considered the next chapter! Ellie has been great help in transcribing my speech, in proofreading, and helping to create the book.

My major academic acknowledgments are to Angela Fawcett, my collaborator for many years and, together with David Fawcett, the major source of my first hand knowledge about dyslexia. I also acknowledge with great warmth the contributions of the many PhD students and undergraduate students who have made distinctive contributions to our research on dyslexia. I also present acknowledgments within the book at appropriate places.

The figures representing the MIND strengths in section 2.3.4 are reproduced with the kind permission of Brock and Fernette Eide. The figures in section 5.7.7 on Goal Mapping are reproduced with the kind permission of Brian Mayne.

Finally, in a picture-rich book like this one, I have presented the work of many people - artists, academics, authors - in thumbnails when describing their work. I believe that this show-cases their work while providing a much more valuable experience for the reader.

The superb photograph on the cover is from the Shutterstock collection of Sergey Borisov. It is the Temple of Poseidon at Cape Sounion in Greece, and I have chosen it to represent the dawn of the age of Positive Dyslexia, with the sun rising over the 'Temple of Strengths' for the dyslexia decathlon.

Preface

Dyslexia has become seen purely as a disability. Positive Dyslexia turns this around, applying the insights of Positive Psychology to guide all dyslexic people in finding, developing and living their strengths. As the founder of Positive Dyslexia, I have written this book to highlight that - given the right opportunities - dyslexic people have distinctive and important strengths to be nurtured rather than an affliction to be tolerated.

In longstanding research with Angela Fawcett we established that the weakness of automatic 'brain-based' learning in dyslexia can be counter-balanced by strengths in 'mind-based' learning. This 'Delayed Neural Commitment' framework leads to the controversial but incontrovertible claim that we are actually exacerbating - and maybe causing - the problems of dyslexia by 'hot-housing' early formal instruction before the necessary neural circuits have matured. The 'neural abscesses' caused by the ensuing inescapable failure essentially disable learning in a reading context.

Turning to the positive, if this damage can be avoided or alleviated, the strengths of dyslexic children, when encouraged, can lead to what I call the 'Strengths Decathlon' of work skills, cognitive skills and social skills, arguably the most important skills for success as an individual, or as an organization in the 21st century.

As befits its title, the book is not only positive, but also constructive, providing and exploring a complete blueprint for the 'dyslexia journey,' taking a dyslexic child from birth through early, middle and late school right through to success in life. I conclude that we must recognize and foster 'Talent Diversity' in work, University and school.

The book presents a stimulating challenge for everyone. It's intellectually challenging. I present state-of-the-art knowledge from six disciplines, weaving them together by means of the dyslexia journey. It also challenges established views. Dyslexia has attracted a range of strongly held, diverse views. I expect the response of the dyslexia community to be overwhelmingly positive, but there will be considerable debate which will, I hope, lead to significant progress not only for dyslexic people but also for our approaches in school, work and society.

The book is also highly original, initially with the very concept of Positive Dyslexia, and then the discovery of the Dyslexia Decathlon of skills, the delayed neural commitment theory, the 'neural abscess' insight, the Dyslexia Work Strengths Finder, and finally the Talent Diversity framework.

Positive Dyslexia attempts to engage everyone, whether dyslexic or not, and covers perspectives of positive psychology, education, cognitive neuroscience, management and human potential and fulfillment. There's something for everyone, from academics to parents, and I hope this will empower a generation of adults and children to make a difference to the way we run our lives.

Sheffield, March 2015

Table of Contents

Positive Dyslexia Overview

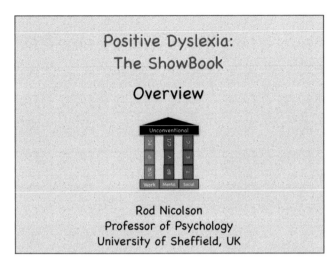

Welcome, and thank you very much for letting me share my obsession with you. I am Roderick Nicolson, Professor of Psychology at the University of Sheffield, in the heart of England.

For the past 25 years I have had the privilege of working at the forefront of dyslexia research and practice. And my obsession is to make a real difference by shattering the shackles that drag down the dyslexia community and dyslexic individuals.

In this book I develop a vision, which I call Positive Dyslexia, where the strengths of dyslexia are not just acknowledged but actually coveted.

This Temple represents the strengths of dyslexia - with one pillar for the three 'Social Strengths' (Teamwork, Empathy and Communication), one for the three 'Cognitive Strengths' (Big Picture, Visualization and Creativity-Innovation), and one for the three 'Work Strengths' (Determination-Resilience, Proactivity and Flexible Coping), all capped and integrated by a strength in 'Unconventional Thinking'.

I call these ten skills the 'Dyslexia Decathlon' and in the course of the book I demonstrate not only that these skills are characteristic of dyslexia, but also that they are precisely the skills needed for individuals and organizations to flourish in the 21st Century.

Chapter 1: Positive Dyslexia

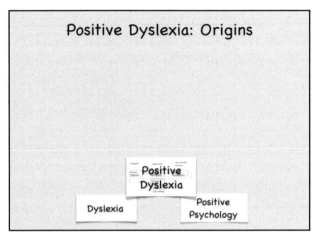

My Positive Dyslexia journey started off when I was reading a book by Martin Seligman, the founder of the Positive Psychology movement.

Curing the Negatives does not Produce the Positives.

What a profound insight! Seligman was talking about depression and the like, but it's just as true for dyslexia. No-one will ever employ you because your reading has got less bad - they will employ you because of your strengths

This made me realize just how dangerous and one-sided is the emphasis on dyslexia as a disability.

Three years later in 2012, with Thomas West and Brock Eide, we were giving the inaugural symposium on Positive Dyslexia at the IDA Parents' Convention.

Taking the lead both from dyslexia research and from Positive Psychology, we argued that we must create a new discipline, Positive Dyslexia, whereby dyslexic people can work to their strengths not their weaknesses.

The figure illustrates the first two building blocks in place, providing the foundations for the new discipline on which I build throughout this book.

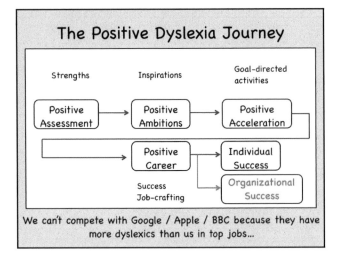

The Positive Dyslexia Journey is my attempt to map out a 'blueprint' for Positive Dyslexia. This drives the movement.

We start with a Positive Assessment which focuses on strengths, because they - not weaknesses - are the key to success.

Next we try to encourage Positive Ambitions, to dream bigger dreams. Here for each career path, we find inspiring role models - dyslexic people who have succeeded in that career.

These ambitions then set up the appropriate 'pull goals', and we try to accelerate progress toward these goals by whatever methods are effective.

This should then lead to a career that suits the strengths. And once in a career it should be possible to craft the job to your strengths and goals, leading to individual success.

And in a recent addition, I realized that if we are to 'rebrand' dyslexia in terms of strengths, we need the bosses of the companies to realize that actually dyslexia is a resource, providing important skills, rather than a burden for them.

The quote "We can't compete with Google / Apple / BBC because they have more dyslexics than us in top jobs" represents the transformation in employment status that we need to create.

Positive Dyslexia is my attempt to walk the walk, to map out the journey

Chapter 2: Strengths of Dyslexia

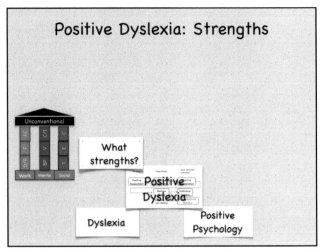

Working with Sara Agahi, I therefore started by investigating the strengths of successful dyslexic adults and entrepreneurs. These strengths can be categorized in terms of three strengths triads:

- The Work Skills Triad of determination, proactivity and flexible coping.
- the Cognitive Skills Triad of big picture thinking, creativity and visualization, and
- the Social Skills Triad of teamwork, empathy and communication.

These nine strengths are then integrated and capped by strengths in Unconventional Thinking, leading to my idea of the Dyslexia Decathlon.

Chapter 3: Why Dyslexia

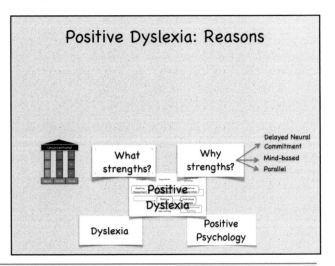

My next aim was to understand the underlying causes of these strengths. In my research with Angela Fawcett, we have discovered that dyslexic children learn differently - not worse, differently - their brains are less 'plastic', needing longer to build the necessary circuitry and habits.

The upside of this reduced plasticity - which I call Delayed Neural Commitment - is greater potential strengths in conscious, parallel, mind-based learning, compensating for the weakness in sequential, brain-based, stimulus-response habits.

Chapter 4: Sinking

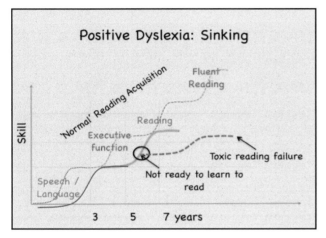

Unfortunately, the downside of Delayed Neural Commitment shows up well before any potential benefits. The result of delayed neural commitment is that dyslexic children need considerably longer, or considerably more favorable circumstances, to learn specific skills, and - even more damaging - they need longer experience to build the neural circuits that are needed to benefit from class-based teaching. This has serious implications for reading readiness.

The figure shows the standard process of reading instruction - it depends both on skill learning and the maturation of the neural circuits for executive function. School-based instruction is designed so these normally coincide

Because of delayed neural commitment, dyslexic children are not ready to learn to read at five years, because they have not yet created the executive function circuits needed to learn via class-based instruction. Attempts to 'hot-house' the learning process without the necessary brain circuits leads to

learning failure, then the trauma of 'toxic reading failure'.

Chapter 4: Failing to Learn, Learning to Fail

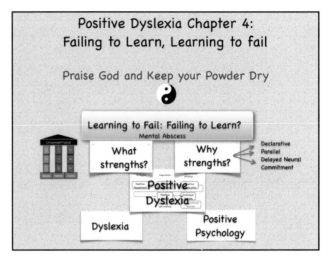

Chapter 4 represents a diversion from the positive approach, and indeed it extends the general approach of Positive Psychology. Martin Seligman recognized from the outset that Positive Psychology was intended to complement traditional approaches, but in fact a truly effective approach has to combine both the positive and the negative, to create a synergy between them.

This was of course well understood by the only successful English revolutionary, Oliver Cromwell, who instructed his men not only to trust in God - the Positive Side, but also to keep their Powder Dry - attending to the negative! It was also known to the Chinese I-Ching as the yin and yang 3000 years ago!

Failing to Learn: Learning to Fail - what do I mean by the chapter title?

I was concerned by the disproportionate numbers of dyslexic children that fail, even ending up in jail. I reviewed all the academic literature - learned helplessness, stress, epigenetics, affective neuroscience, math anxiety - to establish the likely effects of such trauma on subsequent mental well-being and learning potential. I was appalled by my findings. My key discovery here is that repeated failures in class can lead to what I call 'mental abscesses' and learned helplessness in the school situation - as I explain next.

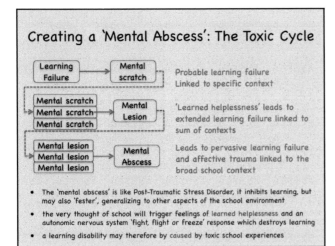

Each individual learning failure leads to what I call a 'mental scratch'. This scratch will be specifically linked to the context in which it occurred. No problem by itself, it will heal with time or following a success.

Repeated mental scratches, however, if not given the opportunity to heal, will lead to what I call a 'mental lesion' - a deeper cut that can lead to a 'learned helplessness' that actively prevents learning in that extended context, and therefore is likely to cause significant future problems. Even so, a lesion can heal given time and the right treatment.

Repeated mental lesions, unfortunately, lead to deeper, near-permanent 'mental abscesses'. This 'mental abscess' is like Post-Traumatic Stress Disorder, it inhibits learning, but may also 'fester', generalizing to other aspects of the school environment.

The very thought of school will trigger feelings of learned helplessness and an autonomic nervous system 'fight, flight or freeze' response which destroys learning.

A learning disability may therefore be caused by toxic school experiences.

Succeeding with Dyslexia

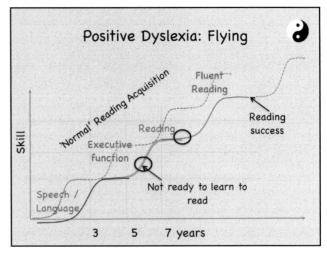

Having identified the dangers, the dark side, I then move back to the positive.

If these catastrophic problems are avoided - which in my view is best achieved pre-school by utilizing individual, playful apps to provide the necessary foundations and where necessary, by delaying formal instruction - the delayed neural commitment can lead to a range a benefits.

Furthermore, unlike the conventional brain - which is likely to be set in its ways by early adulthood - delayed neural commitment allows the dyslexic adult to keep learning, thereby continuing to develop experience-related strengths.

Chapter 5: Succeeding in School

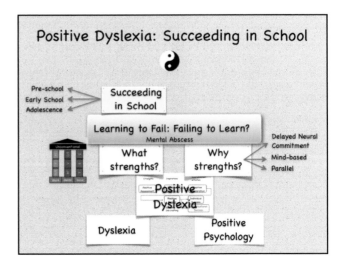

Armed with the knowledge of the dark side, I then go through my 'Succeeding with Dyslexia' trilogy.

First Succeeding in School, providing ideas for pre-School, where individualized apps can be used to 'inoculate' the infant from the risks of toxic learning, to early school, where the key is to supplement the reading program, to adolescence, where the keys to overcoming mental abscesses are adaptation, inspiration, acceleration and reconfiguration.

Chapter 6: Succeeding in Work

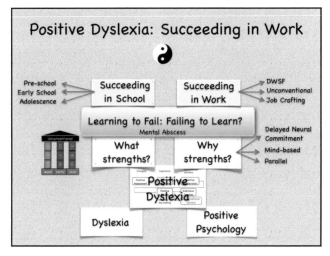

The next Chapter covers Succeeding in Work. A core idea is the Dyslexia Work Strengths Finder, which I have developed with Sara Agahi. Our research using University students indicated a very clear preference for unconventional careers in the dyslexic students - Holland's Artistic and Social types. The study also confirmed that the dyslexic students had distinctive strengths in the Cognitive and the Social Skills Triads, but not in the Work Skills Triad, suggesting that work strengths are still developing at University age.

The Chapter also gives a lightning tour of how - as a dyslexic adult - to write your resumé, get your first job, negotiate it to your strengths, get your next job, and craft your job to your motivations, skills and passions.

Chapter 7: Succeeding in Society

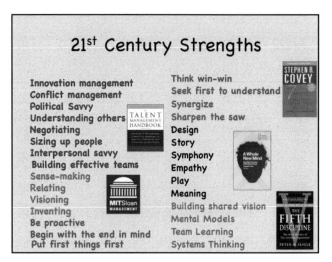

My capstone chapter was inspired by the Positive Psychology approach to character strengths in which Seligman, Peterson and their colleagues analyzed the great religions and philosophies to identify recurring and overlapping themes. I analyzed the core texts in talent, in management, in human capital and on competition to identify the distinctive strengths that are crucial for 21st century success.

My analyses revealed this set of 24 strengths:

- 8 Hard-to-develop skills from the Talent Management Handbook. 8 Special skills:
- 4 Capabilities from the MIT Sloan 4 Capabilities Leadership framework.
- 7 Habits, from Stephen Covey's blockbuster.
- 6 senses, from Dan Pink's analysis of the 21st century strengths.
- 4 of the 5 disciplines from Peter Senge's analysis of the requirements for the Learning Organization.

I then categorized them into work strengths, mental strengths and social strengths.

24 Work Strengths, Cognitive Strengths and Social Strengths

21st Century Strengths

Work Strengths	Mental Strengths	Social Strengths
Be proactive	Synergize	Think win-win
Sharpen the saw	Inventing	Seek first to understand
	Sense-making	Relating
	Design	**Conflict management**
	Visioning	**Political Savvy**
	Story	**Understanding others**
	Symphony	**Negotiating**
	Mental Models	**Sizing up people**
	Put first things first	**Interpersonal savvy**
	Begin with the end	**Building effective teams**
	in mind	Team Learning
	Meaning	Building shared vision
	Innovation management	**Empathy**
Play	Systems Thinking	

It can be seen that the results are really interesting - I have not managed to place Play, and there are few work strengths (I suspect that is because the Work Strengths are the Conventional strengths that characterized the 20th century approach).

But there are lots of mental strengths and social strengths.

So how do these correspond to the strengths triads that we found characterized dyslexia?

21st Century Strengths and the Dyslexia Decathlon

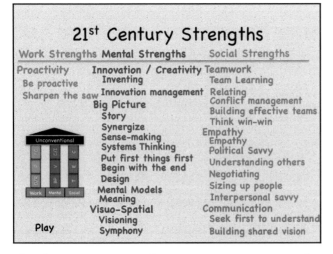

21st Century Strengths

Work Strengths	Mental Strengths	Social Strengths
Proactivity	**Innovation / Creativity**	Teamwork
Be proactive	Inventing	Team Learning
Sharpen the saw	Innovation management	Relating
	Big Picture	Conflict management
	Story	Building effective teams
	Synergize	Think win-win
	Sense-making	Empathy
	Systems Thinking	Empathy
	Put first things first	Political Savvy
	Begin with the end	Understanding others
	Design	Negotiating
	Mental Models	Sizing up people
	Meaning	Interpersonal savvy
	Visuo-Spatial	Communication
	Visioning	Seek first to understand
Play	Symphony	Building shared vision

The figure rearranges the 24 21st century strengths into the categories of the Dyslexia Decathlon.

We have found 7 of the 9 characteristic skills of dyslexia - for the Work Skills Triad we have Proactivity, but Determination / Resilience isn't there, and neither is Flexible coping.

But all three mental strengths are strongly represented - Innovation, Big Picture, Visuo-Spatial.

As are the Social Skills Triad - Teamwork, Empathy. Communication.

Isn't this remarkable! The strengths of dyslexia are precisely those required for individuals, organizations and societies to succeed in the 21st century!

The Talent Diversity Proposal

Talent Diversity

- Diversity in terms of gender, culture and age is already fully established as beneficial both for equity and for effectiveness
- For any organization it is equally vital to have a balance of talents – talent diversity – since otherwise there is a danger of groupthink and stagnation.
- Most organizations focus, for recruitment and promotion, on the 20th century talents of analysis, rational thinking, planning, target completion.
- But what about the important unconventional talents? These are employees who can provide competitive advantage in the 21st century, and should be identified and cherished.
- Every organization has dyslexic employees. These employees represent an untapped source of unconventional talents, and it should be a management priority for any organization to identify, 'design in', and manage talent diversity.

These considerations lead to my inclusive proposal, based on the idea of balance - the yin and the yang of talents. In this case I am highlighting the need both for the traditional conventional strengths, and for the unconventional strengths characteristic of, but not limited to, dyslexia.

The idea here is 'talent diversity' and is even more applicable to the conventional organization - such as government departments, HR departments, city halls - than to the unconventional, creative, entrepreneurial companies.

Diversity in terms of gender, culture and age is already fully established as beneficial both for equity and for effectiveness .

For any organization it is equally vital to have a balance of talents - talent diversity - since otherwise there is a danger of groupthink and stagnation.

Most organizations focus, for recruitment and promotion, on the 20th century talents of analysis, rational thinking, planning, target completion.

But what about the important unconventional talents? These are the 'wealth creators', the employees who can provide competitive advantage in the 21st Century.

Every organization has dyslexic employees. These employees represent an untapped source of unconventional talents, and it should be a management priority for any organization to identify, 'design in' and manage talent diversity.

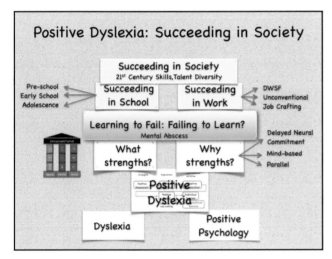

My capstone chapter 'Succeeding in Society' concludes by advocating the concept of Talent Diversity, and how it is important for all organizations to create a balance in the human capital resources between unconventional and conventional skills, and to recruit to their Talent Management programs workers with the appropriate type of skills.

This has major implications not just for Human Resources departments and for the success of companies and organizations, but actually the whole of society - our beliefs, our goals, our universities and our schools.

Diversity of Talents will not be achieved by hot-housing, drilling or by forcing but, as with adult learning, by engaging, by playing, by following your star.

We have the tools, the conceptual framework, the belief and the imperative to achieve this.

Positive Dyslexia MIND-map

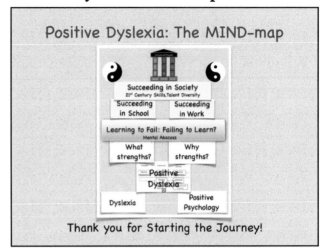

So, this is the big picture for Positive Dyslexia. The core idea throughout is that of Balance and Synergy - between work on disabilities and work on abilities, between traditional and innovative teaching methods, and between conventional and unconventional talents.

I have called it a MIND-map to resonate with Tony Buzan's mind-mapping techniques for visual thinkers, and Brock and Fernette Eide's MIND strengths from their inspirational book, the Dyslexic Advantage

Finally, it is discourteous to force dyslexic people to read a book, so I have created this book with as strong a visual narrative as possible, using this 'advance organiser' to give you the helicopter view, and so that each page may be seen as self-contained. I also provide an index, glossary and contents list.

I hope this will let you skim, focus or search as as you prefer.

But, however you use it, please enjoy the Positive Dyslexia story. I hope it will inspire you.

Thank you for starting the Positive Dyslexia Journey.

Chapter 1: Introduction

1.1 Origins of Positive Dyslexia

Positive Dyslexia

Chapter 1:
Introduction

Rod Nicolson
Professor of Psychology
University of Sheffield, UK

Symposium
Positive Dyslexia:
Working to our Strengths

1. Rod Nicolson: Positive Dyslexia: Follow Your Stars
2. Sara Agahi: Strengths of Dyslexia in the workplace: A Positive Psychology approach
3. Thomas West: Dyslexia: A Strengths Approach
4. Brock Eide: Understanding and Fostering the Cognitive Advantages in Individuals with Dyslexia
5. Forum

Symposium presented at
IDA Parents Conference, Baltimore
October 2012

For the past 25 years, as Professor of Psychology at the University of Sheffield in the United Kingdom, I have had the privilege of being associated with progress in dyslexia research, nationally and internationally.

Working with Tim Miles early on and with Angela Fawcett throughout, I have had the good fortune to discover three of the most important theories for dyslexia, published the first screening tests that could be used by teachers to identify children at risk of dyslexia before they learned to read, and I was proud to chair the 2001 BDA International Conference.

I am not saying everyone agreed with me. Indeed I was shortlisted for the 'heretic of the year' award in the late 1990s.

But in all my research I have focused on the weaknesses of dyslexia. I think it's time to set this record straight.

I am basing this introductory chapter on the talk I gave at the inaugural symposium on Positive Dyslexia, which took place at the Inaugural Parents' Conference in the International Dyslexia Association Meeting in Baltimore, Maryland [1, 2].

This took place in late October 2012, just before Hurricane Sandy devastated the US eastern seaboard. In this talk I explained the background to Positive Dyslexia and presented a 'roadmap' for progress over the next few years.

I was particularly proud to have the opportunity to share the platform with two of the best selling, and most positive, writers about dyslexia, Thomas West and Brock Eide, and I was also delighted to be able to introduce one of the most positive people I know, my PhD student, Sara Agahi.

Since the rest of the book follows this roadmap, I feel that this is good way of starting the journey that is represented in this book, and will, I hope, be taken further by you, the readers.

1.1.1 Dedication: Professor Tim Miles

Dedication: Professor T. R. Miles

... It was again a medical man, Dr. Orton, who in the 1920s and 1930s called attention to this group of difficulties. I think it can fairly be claimed that Orton did more than any other early pioneer to put dyslexia 'on the map'.

... For the next two decades, however (that is, in the 1940s and 1950s), it appears that large-scale educational measurements were in fashion rather than the detailed study of individual cases ... It may be my personal prejudice, but I have serious doubts as to whether such surveys provide data of any lasting significance, and I certainly wish that researchers had spent more time looking at individual children.

Dyslexia: the Pattern of Difficulties (1983 p. 3)

I dedicated my presentation to the late Professor Tim Miles, a wonderful man who completed 50 years in dyslexia research and was the founder of the Bangor Dyslexia Unit.

Tim was an inspirational figure in British dyslexia research, and he fought long and hard to maintain the 'community' of dyslexia, welcoming dyslexic children and parents just as warmly as dyslexia researchers.

He founded the journal 'Dyslexia' specifically to maintain both scientific and applied research - research that might be hard to include within 'standard' scientific journals.

This quotation, from his influential 1983 book, 'Dyslexia: the Pattern of Difficulties', gives a feel for his approach.

"It was again a medical man, Dr. Orton, who in the 1920s and 1930s called attention to this group of difficulties. I think it can fairly be claimed that Orton did more than any other early pioneer to put dyslexia 'on the map'.

... For the next two decades, however (that is, in the 1940s and 1950s), it appears that large-scale educational measurements were in fashion rather than the detailed study of individual cases ... It may be my personal prejudice, but I have serious doubts as to whether such surveys provide data of any lasting significance, and I certainly wish that researchers had spent more time looking at individual children" [3].

This quotation highlights his emphasis throughout on the individual rather than the statistic. It's an emphasis that is absolutely crucial, but has been lost in recent times.

1.1.2 Plan of Chapter 1

Plan of Chapter 1

1. Dyslexia: The Yin and the Yang
2. The Dyslexia Ecosystem
3. Positive Psychology
4. Positive Dyslexia
5. What we can do...

Let me give you the plan for this first chapter. This is the overview of my talk in the symposium. This chapter is essentially the same, but I have taken the opportunity to provide more information about dyslexia, and to introduce the inspiring film by Harvey Hubbell entitled 'Dislecksia, the Movie':

- Dyslexia: The Yin and the Yang - the upside and the downside
- The Dyslexia Ecosystem
- Positive Psychology
- Positive Dyslexia
- What we can do...

1.2 Developmental Dyslexia

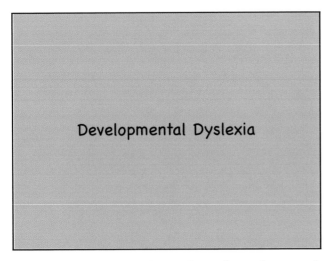

I start off with a brief overview of Developmental Dyslexia.

1.2.1 Definitions of Developmental Dyslexia

I will start with the traditional definition. This is the classic definition, and the one that was current when I first became interested in dyslexia, 25 years ago [4].

Note the emphasis on three separate abilities.

"a disorder in children who, despite conventional classroom experience, fail to attain the language skills of reading, writing and spelling commensurate with their intellectual abilities."

But I need to note that everything is in terms of weaknesses, of problems, of changing scores from -5 to -3. Let me continue by giving another quote in a highly cited article by Sally Shaywitz in the New England Journal of Medicine in 1998 [5].

"Developmental dyslexia is characterized by an unexpected difficulty in children and adults who otherwise possess the intelligence, motivation and schooling considered necessary for accurate and fluent reading."

One key aspect in both of these definitions is the unexpectedness of the problem. This relates to the discrepancy idea - that there is a discrepancy between the child's reading ability and that expected on the basis of the child's general intelligence.

The issue of discrepancy is controversial, in that it depends on the problematic concept of general intelligence, and it has been fiercely criticized by reading researchers, starting with a seminal article by Linda Siegel in 1989, in the belief that the optimal method to teach reading is independent of a child's intelligence [6].

Nonetheless, the idea of unexpectedness is central to the concept of dyslexia, and in my view key to understanding the underlying causes of dyslexia. If there is a discrepancy between reading and other skills, then there are relative strengths in areas outside reading. The basis of Positive Dyslexia is that if we identify these strengths, and attempt to develop them further, this will be of great benefit to the individual concerned.

1.2.2 The Paradox of Dyslexia

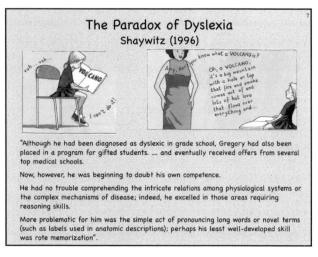

Sally Shaywitz, Director of the Yale Center, highlights the paradox of dyslexia, illustrating it, in a Scientific American article, by the little girl who cannot read the word 'volcano' but is able to give a fluent description of what a volcano is - "Oh, a VOLCANO, it's a big mountain with a hole on top that fire and smoke come out of and lots of hot lava that flows over everything..." and so on [7].

She also provides a case study of Gregory, who had extreme difficulties in reading and in rote memorization, but nevertheless was able to perform at high academic levels,

These are prototypical cases for the strengths of dyslexia. I will give many such case studies in the second chapter.

"Although he had been diagnosed as dyslexic in grade school, Gregory had also been placed in a program for gifted students. .... and eventually received offers from several top medical schools.

Now, however, he was beginning to doubt his own competence.

He had no trouble comprehending the intricate relations among physiological systems or the complex mechanisms of disease; indeed, he excelled in those areas requiring reasoning skills.

More problematic for him was the simple act of pronouncing long words or novel terms (such as labels used in anatomic descriptions); perhaps his least well-developed skill was rote memorization."

These are prototypical cases for the strengths of dyslexia. I will give you many such cases in the second chapter.

1.2.3 Dislecksia the Movie

Arguably the most directly relevant use of the talents of dyslexia is by Harvey Hubbell, a dyslexic film maker.

Harvey has created a full length film on dyslexia, Dislecksia the Movie, to highlight the damage it causes to self-esteem, the lack of understanding of the general population, and the large numbers of highly successful dyslexic adults [8].

This is his own personal statement of his early years, together with an analysis by Gordon Sherman, a leading academic and educator for dyslexia.

Both highlight the unexpectedness of the difficulties, and the trauma caused in early school (and after).

Quotations from Dislecksia the Movie

Dislecksia the Movie

- I was a happy kid. I grew up in the early 60s. Life was good back then. I had a spring in my step and not a care in the world ... I was like every other kid ... life was good.
And then I went to school.
I did NOT have a great time at elementary school. I moved from a happy kid to a child with severe perceptual problem.
Harvey Hubbell – Dislecksia the Movie

- Pre-school, kindergarten, first, second grade this kid who's dyslexic has been doing fine. Third grade - bang – hits the wall, and all at once this kid is not able to do what the other kids in the class are doing. And starts to wonder "what's going on here?".
And things get worse and worse.
Gordon Sherman – Dislecksia the Movie

"I was a happy kid. I grew up in the early 60s. Life was good back then. I had a spring in my step and not a care in the world ... I was like every other kid ... life was good. And then I went to school.

I did NOT have a great time at elementary school. I moved from a happy kid to a child with severe perceptual problem."

And then a quote from Gordon Sherman, the very influential dyslexia researcher and now educationalist.

"Pre-school, kindergarten, first, second grade this kid who's dyslexic has been doing fine. Third grade - bang hits the wall, and all at once this kid is not able to do what the other kids in the class are doing. And starts to wonder 'what is going on here?' And things get worse and worse."

1.2.5 Reasons for high interest in dyslexia

Reasons for high interest in dyslexia

1. high incidence in Western populations
(~5-10% is a typical estimate, Badian, 1984; Jorm et al, 86)

2. high financial stakes
(statutory requirement in many Western countries to provide educational support for children with dyslexia).

3. Challenging paradox to a wide variety of researchers — why do these articulate, intelligent people show such a problem in one of our most routine skills?

→ Continuing high international public profile
e.g. US NICHD (National Institute of Child Health and Human Development) dyslexia funding now at least $15m p.a. since 1985

I had best give a bit more formal background to dyslexia research and practice. There are reasons for high interest in dyslexia:

- There is a high incidence in Western populations of 5-10%.

- There are high financial stakes, with a statutory requirement in many Western countries to provide educational support for children with dyslexia.

- Dyslexia presents a challenging paradox to a wide variety of researchers - why do these articulate, intelligent people show such a problem in one of our most routine skills?

And this has meant there is a continuing high international public profile for dyslexia. For instance, the US National Institute of Child Health and Human Development has been funding dyslexia (or at least reading) at the rate of at least $15m per year since 1985.

1.2.6 My message

1.2.7 Dyslexia: The key questions

My message - and this is the start of the talk I gave at the 2012 IDA Conference - is on the one hand the Dyslexia community has made outstanding progress in terms of Awareness, Legislation and Research - which is all good.

But on the other hand, this has been at the expense of Disability, Disempowerment, Disengagement and Despair.

- The focus on Disability rather than Ability, 'No child left behind' rather than 'every child succeeding'.
- The focus on 'leave it to the professionals, there is nothing you can do to help your child.'
- The result that many parents become disenchanted and disengaged with dyslexia associations.
- And despair as one's child suffers at school.

It is time to ask the right questions.

I am taking the view that it is now time to turn to the positive side!

To make progress one needs to know what one is trying to achieve.

Many researchers see things only from their own perspective. Most dyslexia researchers are interested primarily in the question of "how we can improve the reading of dyslexic children and adults" because that is their speciality.

That is a worthy goal, but there are enough researchers doing it. For me, as an applied researcher, the first priority must be to ask the intended beneficiary what they really want. These are the answers I hear:

- The Worker says "How can I be respected and valued for my abilities?"
- The Parent says "How can my child have a happy and fulfilled life?"
- And the Researcher should say "How can we make the most theoretical and applied progress?"

And we really do have a new generation of tools, the science, the answers that will transform the field over the next five years.

1.2.8 Key Points

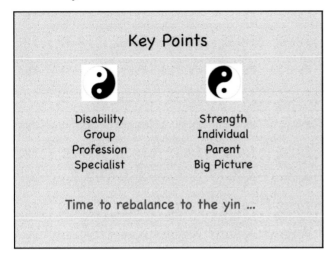

I first became interested in dyslexia in the late 1980s when a mature student, Angela Fawcett, the mother of a dyslexic boy around 10 years old at the time, persuaded me to supervise her doctoral research.

I was fortunate to benefit from the wisdom of Tim Miles, and Ingvar Lundberg, the major figures in European dyslexia research, and also of the amazing Rodin Remediation Academy, funded by Per Udden, which aimed to broaden the horizons of dyslexia researchers by bringing in the best of research in related fields such as cognitive neuroscience and expertise.

Tim was a 'big picture' dyslexia researcher. He was also a 'big tent' dyslexia researcher, aiming to include all dyslexia researchers, and all dyslexic people within the dyslexia community. Unfortunately he was fighting an uphill battle against the increasing specialization, compartmentalization and professionalization of science.

This figure indicates the tensions between the two approaches the specialist versus the generalist. It is not that either is wholly right or wholly wrong. It is just that one needs a balance between the two.

The key point I want to make is that we have made great progress with specialist research - on disability, on group work, on the professional approach and specialism, but now the time is now ripe for more inclusive research that looks at strengths, the individual, the parent and the Big Picture.

It is time to rebalance to the Yin!

1.3 Dyslexia as Deficit

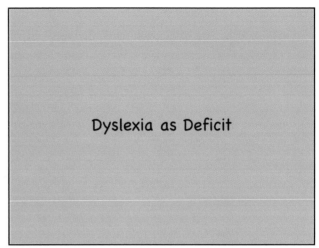

In case, like me until recently, you had not noticed the pervasive and pernicious scope of the 'dyslexia as deficit' perspective, I will just give you a couple of pointers on how dyslexia is currently seen in principle, in practice and in theory.

1.3.1 Deficit Definition of Dyslexia

Here first is the Deficit Definition of Dyslexia. This is from the International Dyslexia Association Definition.

"Dyslexia is a specific learning disability that is neurological in origin. It is characterized by difficulties with accurate and/or fluent word recognition and by poor spelling and decoding abilities. These difficulties typically result from a deficit in the phonological component of language that is often unexpected in relation to other cognitive abilities and the provision of effective classroom instruction. Secondary consequences may include problems in reading comprehension and reduced reading experience that can impede the growth of vocabulary and background knowledge" [9].

I hate this definition.

 Look at those --- disability, difficulties, poor spelling, difficulties, deficit, problems, impede! The only concession to strengths is the phrase highlighted in blue "unexpected in relation to other cognitive abilities."

Worse, this deficit framework applies throughout - diagnosis for adults is also in terms of weaknesses, theories are phrased in terms of 'what deficits and why?' And school education appears to focus only on deficits and their remediation.

This really needs changing!

1.4 The Big Picture: Dyslexia Ecosystem

> **The Big Picture:**
> **The Positive Dyslexia Ecosystem**

I did my best as Chair of the 2001 6th British Dyslexia Association international conference to provide a theoretical underpinning for the inclusive approach by introducing the concept of 'the Dyslexia Ecosystem'.

This is a concept I developed in discussion with the great Swedish dyslexia researcher, Ingvar Lundberg.

1.4.1 The Dyslexia Community

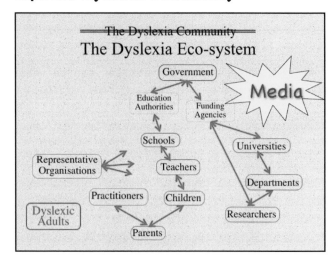

The core insight here is that a community is more complex than just the sum of its parts, and that in order for a community to thrive it is necessary to take a holistic view.

Here I try to show that the standard analytical approach of specializing on just one aspect will lead to a series of destructive 'zero-sum' games.

For example:

We have Children, we have Researchers. The Researchers are trying to gain money from their Departments, the Departments are trying to gain money from their Universities, their Universities are trying to gain money from the government. The researchers are also trying to gain money from the Funding Agencies. These are all 'zero sum games' - if one researcher wins, the others lose.

Children the same - the children are trying to gain time and effort from the teachers, the teachers are trying time and resources from the school ... and the school from the education authorities, and the education authorities from the government. All zero sum games.

The parents are also trying to get more time for their children. The parents are also trying to get help from the practitioners. The representative organizations are also trying to get more time and resources for their own particular organization.

Dyslexic adults do not seem to come into this picture at all.

The whole thing is just stirred up by the media.

In short, there is a high risk that the pursuit of individual advantage is detrimental to the well-being of the overall community.

Consequently, I suggested that we should replace the idea of a dyslexia community by the Dyslexia Ecosystem.

1.4.2 The Dyslexia Ecosystem

The Dyslexia Ecosystem [18]

- It is all too easy, in everyday interactions in dyslexia, to see the interactions in a semi-adversarial fashion – parents competing to get more support for children, researchers competing to get more support for their theories, schools trying to get more money for their programmes.
  - 'zero-sum'. If one party gains, the other one loses.
- If, by contrast, one views the dyslexia community as a complex, inter-dependent 'ecosystem', a much more positive view emerges. It becomes clear that there are solutions for the system as a whole
  - 'win-win', that is, all parties gain and none lose.
- … there is in fact a clear, shared, goal 'to develop significantly improved support for dyslexic infants, children and adults in an effective but cost-effective fashion'.   Nicolson (2002, pp. 55, 62)
- I now think we can do much better – we can develop a system so that every dyslexic individual can work and live to his or her strengths. This is the goal of Positive Dyslexia.

The ecosystem is actually the whole system.

"It is all too easy, in everyday interactions in dyslexia, to see the interactions in a semi-adversarial fashion - parents competing to get more support for children, researchers competing to get more support for their theories, schools trying to get more money for their programs.

'Zero-sum' - if one party gains, the other one loses.

If, by contrast, one views the dyslexia community as a complex, inter-dependent 'eco-system', a much more positive view emerges. It becomes clear that there are solutions for the system as a whole

'Win-win', that is, all parties gain and none lose.

… there is in fact a clear, shared, goal 'to develop significantly improved support for dyslexic infants, children and adults in an effective but cost-effective fashion.'"

That was an article I wrote back in 2002 for the Dyslexia journal. It is the advantage, I think, of big picture thinking, trying to see the system as a whole [10].

The problem of course is that most of the players were more intent on securing their own competitive advantage against their perceived rivals, and my pleas fell on deaf ears.

But now - and this is a major point - I think we can do much better even than the ecosystem, we can develop a system so that every dyslexic individual can work and live to his or her strengths. This is the goal of Positive Dyslexia.

1.4.3 Martin Seligman - Curing the negatives does not produce the positives

Martin Seligman
Positive Psychology
Preface to Learned Optimism, 2nd ed

… But clinical psychologists also began to find something disconcerting emerging from therapy: even on that rare occasion when therapy goes superbly and unusually well, and you help the client rid herself of depression, anxiety, and anger, happiness is not guaranteed. Emptiness is not an uncommon result.

… Curing the negatives does not produce the positives. … The skills of becoming happy turn out to be almost entirely different from the skills of not being sad, not being anxious, or not being angry.

I had one of those 'road to Damascus' conversions when I read this passage in Martin Seligman's book on Positive Psychology [11].

I had done lots of good things for diagnosing dyslexia so that early support could be given. But it was always in terms of weaknesses, never strengths.

But then I read this passage - Seligman worked on depression.

"… But clinical psychologists also began to find something disconcerting emerging from therapy: even on that rare occasion when therapy goes superbly and unusually well, and you help the client rid herself of depression, anxiety, and anger, happiness is not guaranteed. Emptiness is not an uncommon result.

… Curing the negatives does not produce the positives. … The skills of becoming happy turn out to be almost entirely different from the skills of not being sad, not being anxious, or not being angry."

Curing the negatives (reading, phonology) does not produce the positives.

He is absolutely right, and it works just as much for dyslexia.

No-one would ever employ you because you had largely overcome your reading disability! They will employ you because of your strengths.

1.5 Positive Psychology

Positive Psychology

This brings me on to Positive Psychology.

Along with cognitive neuroscience it is the major development in Psychology this century.

1.5.1 Positive Psychology origins

Positive Psychology

1. In 1998, Martin Seligman (APA President) argued that the focus of Psychology on problems is only one side of the coin
2. Initiated the Positive Psychology movement. This focuses on strengths & building the best in life!
3. Designed not to replace existing fields but supplement them
4. Strong emphasis on empowering the individual

Positive Psychology is not some passing fad.

It has both great academic prestige and profile together with strong uptake in the everyday world.

It was introduced in 1998, by Martin Seligman, who was then the President of the American Psychological Association, who argued that the focus of Psychology on problems is only one side of the coin.

He initiated the Positive Psychology movement which focuses on strengths and building the best in life!

It was designed not to replace existing fields but supplement them and had a strong emphasis on empowering the individual.

It seemed to me absolutely perfect for dyslexia.

1.5.2 Pillars of Positive Psychology

Pillars of Positive Psychology

1. Positive experiences
   happiness, pleasure, & joy
2. Positive individual traits
   character, talents & interests
3. Positive institutions
   families, schools, businesses, communities & societies

- Growing literature captured attention of academics & the media
- A movement not a profession

The pillars of Positive Psychology are three:

- Positive experiences - happiness, pleasure and joy;
- Positive individual traits - character, talents and interests;
- Positive institutions - families, schools, businesses, communities and societies.

The Dyslexia Representative Organizations, including the IDA and the BDA, have made a start on trying to get the positive institutions with initiatives like the BDA's 'Dyslexia-Friendly Schools' but this is just the tip of the iceberg.

We have made negligible progress on positive experiences for dyslexic children and adults.

The growing literature of Positive Psychology

captured the attention of academics and the media. Basically, it is a movement not a profession.

1.5.4 Positive Psychology Concepts

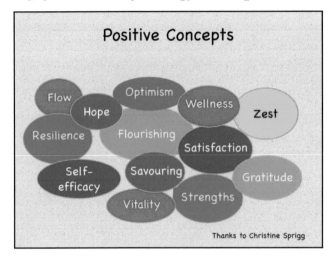

Here are some positive concepts:

Flow, Hope, Optimism, Wellness, Zest, Resilience, Flourishing, Satisfaction, Self-efficacy, Vitality, Savouring, Gratitude, Strengths.

Who would not want more of those in their life!

1.5.5 Positive Psychology Character Strengths

In one of the landmark developments in Positive Psychology, Seligman and Peterson wanted to establish what the character strengths are that everybody values. They studied the world's great religions and philosophies, and tried to establish what were the major underlying themes, common to all.

In fact they came up with 24, in six categories, as shown here:

- Wisdom and Knowledge
- Courage
- Humanity
- Justice
- Temperance
- Transcendence
    Appreciation of Beauty and Excellence, Gratitude, Hope, Humour, and Spirituality.

So these are all Character Strengths. The Values in Action (VIA) website, created by the Mayerson Foundation in 2000, provides the conceptual means of describing positive youth development and a whole series of 'test yourself' Positive Psychology exercises.

1.6 Positive Dyslexia

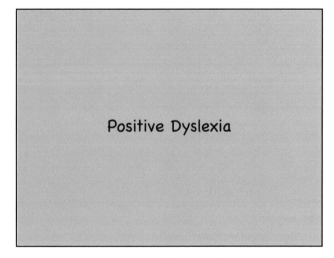

One of the key insights of Positive Psychology is that the life satisfaction scale is not the same for negative and positive experiences. Reducing negative experiences, or weaknesses, is completely different from having positive experiences or building strengths. I hope you see the relevance to dyslexia.

Just as Seligman realized that depression was only considered in terms of negatives, dyslexia is seen by most practitioners in terms of weaknesses

- Diagnosis is by weaknesses.

• Treatment is to limit the weaknesses.

I am reminded of a conversation I had with an able adult dyslexic. He said "If anyone else suggests I have more reading support, I'll throttle them. Been there, got the scars. What I want is something to help me succeed with my dyslexia."

And that is what Positive Dyslexia is all about.

1.6.1 Building and Using Strengths

```
Building and Using Strengths

1. Character Strengths
2. Cognitive Strengths
3. Work Strengths
4. Family Strengths
5. Interests
6. Inspirations
```

But first, a personal view on Positive Psychology. Seligman correctly highlights the fact that it is supposed to supplement existing approaches.

But to be frank, I do have reservations about Positive Psychology. It strikes me that it has the kernel of a brilliant idea, but at the moment it is incomplete - it does not link in with existing approaches.

You seriously cannot get better at reading by only using learned optimism. You need to combine a determined and resilient approach with a good method that suits your strengths of learning. That is, you need to get a synergy between the positive approach and the traditional approach.

So I felt that what we needed was to be broader than Positive Psychology, to go beyond the Character Strengths that Positive Psychology highlights, to consider a range of other strengths, including cognitive strengths, work strengths and experiential strengths.

I also have to say that we need to consider both the Yin and the Yang for a complete approach. It is usually more cost-effective to fix weaknesses in order to be able to work to strengths - as long as we can understand why we are doing it and we can make progress.

1.6.2 Are dyslexic individual more creative than others?

```
Are dyslexic individuals more creative than others?

Wrong Question!
    The answer is, some are, some aren't, and who are you
    comparing with?

The Right Question is the individual one:
    Is creativity one of my relative strengths, and if so,
    what can I do to enhance this strength and craft my
    life to use it?
    The Personal Best...
```

I now move on to this question "Are dyslexic individuals more creative than others?"

There is of course a long and distinguished history of research on strengths and dyslexia, with key proponents being Tom West and Brock Eide. But over the years, they have suffered from being asked to answer this question which though plausible seems to me to be actually designed to force them into a battle they can't win.

I can't stress this strongly enough. The critics are asking the WRONG question.

It makes two unforgivable assumptions:

First that all dyslexics are somehow the same, and therefore it is legitimate to take some group average (or that the control group are all somehow the same)

Second that something like creativity is somehow fixed, and it makes sense to take a snapshot at some age of some aspect of creativity. It's not fixed, and can be substantially improved through training and experience, however creative you are.

The Positive Psychology question is the only one worth asking, the only one with meaning.

Is creativity one of my relative strengths, and if so, what can I do to enhance this strength and craft my life to use it?

The key concept here is the Personal Best. It doesn't matter whether your Personal Best is world-leading or not. It's your Personal Best and you should develop it.

1.6.3 The Positive Approach

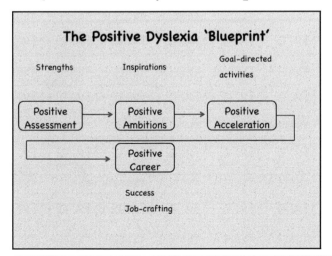

So the Positive Approach is to:

- Identify and empower people to work to their Signature Strengths - working for your own development rather than to someone else's tune

- To identify and guide them toward careers involving their Strengths with better career advice and better diagnostic information

- And to Empower and involve the stakeholders - the parents and the dyslexia associations.

1.6.4 The Positive Dyslexia Blueprint

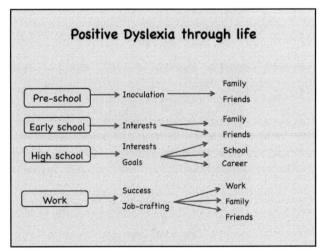

This leads me to what I call the 'Positive Dyslexia Blueprint', which drives the entire initiative.

We start with a Positive Assessment. This does not just look for weaknesses, in the usual fashion. The key requirement is also to look for strengths, because it is the strengths that drive the developments.

Next we try to encourage Positive Ambitions, to dream bigger dreams. Here for the careers where dyslexic individuals tend to have strengths, we try to find inspiring role models, dyslexic people who have succeeded in that career.

Next we try to set up positive acceleration towards those ambitions, so they have appropriate 'pull goals'. We accelerate progress towards these goals by whatever methods are appropriate.

This should lead to appropriate job offers, leading to a career that suits the strengths. And once in a career it should be possible to select those aspects of the job that further suit the strengths - the job crafting.

I have set this up to indicate the complete life process over several years, but there will of course be different priorities for school and work within this general blueprint, as I show next.

1.6.5 Positive Dyslexia through life

There will be different approaches at different stages in life. For a pre-school child, key activities will involve 'inoculating' the child against reading failure. So, pre-school, inoculation, which can be facilitated by family and friends

Remember we need to use the situations that are important to each specific child - their own family and home rather than some generic reading text.

For early school, again the interests are the way to scaffold progress, we have family, friends school for facilitation.

For high school, again use the interests and we can bring in goals, again the friends, the school, the career.

And finally at work, success and job crafting by work, family and friends.

Overall, there are differences at each stage in life, and I am going to take a chapter in the book for each of these different stages.

1.7 Strengths and Dyslexia

Strengths and Dyslexia

But let me now turn to Strengths and Dyslexia. I will just preview the research that has been done in this area. I give a much fuller picture in Chapter 2, but this gives an overview.

1.7.1 Norman Geschwind

Norman Geschwind
(1926-1984)

"We, thus, find that despite the disadvantages of dyslexia, there are advantages both in the unaffected relatives and the sufferers themselves, in the possession, in a very large percentage of cases, of superior talents in certain other areas.

... We are thus brought to the apparently paradoxical notion that the very same anomalies on the left side of the brain that have led to the disability of dyslexia in certain literate societies also determine superiority in the same brains. We can, thus speak of a 'pathology of superiority' without fear of being contradictory!

Why Orton was right (1982 p. 22-23)

Norman Geschwind was a celebrated neuroscientist, and he also turned his attention to dyslexia, taking over from Samuel Orton in trying to understand the underlying brain basis for dyslexia. Consider this quote [12]:

"We, thus, find that despite the disadvantages of dyslexia, there are advantages both in the unaffected relatives and the sufferers themselves, in the possession, in a very large percentage of cases, of superior talents in certain other areas.

... We are thus brought to the apparently paradoxical notion that the very same anomalies on the left side of the brain that have led to the disability of dyslexia in certain literate societies also determine superiority in the same brains. We can, thus speak of a 'pathology of superiority' without fear of being contradictory!"

This quote makes it very clear that Geschwind was convinced that the discrepancy gave the key to understanding dyslexia, and his idea of the 'pathology of superiority' is an attractive and challenging one.

1.7.2 What are the signature strengths of dyslexia?

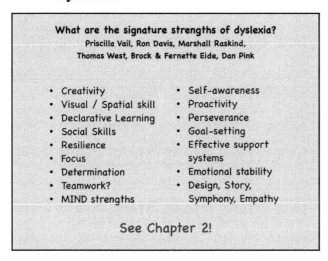

1.7.3 Positive Dyslexia Career Development

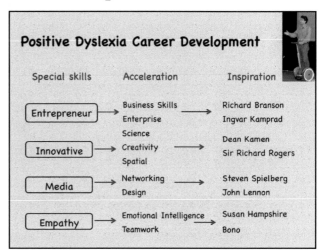

I did not want to steal the thunder from my co-presenters - Sara Agahi was going next, talking about the research which I present in Chapter 2, then Tom West talked about the extraordinary skills - especially visualization - shown by eminent dyslexic adults, then Brock Eide talked about the Dyslexic Advantage, and their MIND strengths framework - so I just showed this summary very briefly.

In fact, this figure is based on the presentation I gave to the British Dyslexia Association conference in Liverpool in 2010 - the first time I had ever thought through Positive Dyslexia and its background. Several of these ideas were actually put forward by the audience.

So here are some of the strengths that have been associated with dyslexia. Also we have suggestions from the literature, with Priscilla Vail, Ron Davis, Marshall Raskind, Thomas West, Brock and Fernette Eide, and Dan Pink contributing to these.

Creativity, Visual / Spatial skill, Declarative Learning, Social Skills, Resilience, Focus, Determination, Teamwork (perhaps), and MIND strengths - that's Brock and Fernette.

Self-awareness, Proactivity, Perseverance, Goal-setting, Effective support systems, Emotional stability, Design, Story, Symphony, Empathy - that's Dan Pink.

I go through their work in much more detail in Chapter 2.

Let me now sketch out the ideas behind Positive Dyslexia career development.

Imagine that you are at high school and your strengths finder has identified that you have entrepreneurial skills.

Then you might get inspiration from some brief talks (available over the Positive Dyslexia app) by well known and successful entrepreneurs like Richard Branson, the founder of Virgin in the UK, or Ingvar Kamprad, founder of IKEA in Sweden, or one of the many well known US dyslexic entrepreneurs.

Having decided that this is the career for you, you will be able to access specific additional skills and social networking opportunities to enhance your chances of making it as an entrepreneur.

Similarly for other classic dyslexia types. If you are innovative - science, creativity or spatial thinking - then the inventor Dean Kamen or the architect Sir Richard Rogers - there's Kamen's Segway vehicle - will be the appropriate inspirations.

Or maybe you're interested in the media - networking, design - Steven Spielberg, John Lennon. These are certainly inspirational figures!

Or maybe empathy, you do not generally get famous for just being empathetic, but empathy underpins the emotional intelligence and teamwork are actually required for actors and performers, such as Susan Hampshire and Bono.

1.8 Conclusions to Chapter 1

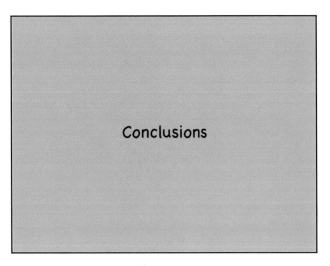

So, I hope this has set the scene.

I have outlined the importance of working to one's strengths.

I have highlighted how mainstream dyslexia research has got completely stuck in the disability rut.

I have outlined a blueprint for the 'dyslexia journey'. This is the journey I have undertaken over the past few years, trying to map the route and to mark the trail.

And the conclusions of my inaugural talk on Positive Dyslexia were extremely positive!

1.8.1 My 2020 Visions.

My 2020 Visions

- Dyslexia in the Workplace
  We cannot compete with [Google / BBC / Virgin etc] because they have more dyslexics than us in top positions
  – opportunity not obligation for the bosses
- Parent
  I know that, if we all work at it, my child has every chance of a successful and fulfilling career and life
  – individual planning and empowerment

We now have the tools and the science to do this

This is where I hope we will be in a few years.

I want the bosses to say:

"We cannot compete with [Google / BBC / Virgin etc] because they have more dyslexics than us in top positions."

That is, it should be an opportunity not an obligation for the bosses.

Second, I want the parent of a dyslexic child to be able to say:

"I know that, if we all work at it, my child has every chance of a successful and fulfilling career and life."

so that we can do the individual planning and empowerment necessary to achieve that.

And this is the key - we now have the tools and the science to achieve this.

1.8.2 Why now?

Why Now?

1. First wave (disability awareness) completed
   - Awareness
   - Legislation
   - Representative bodies
2. The Science is right
   - Positive Psychology
   - Work Psychology
   - Individual Psychology
3. Tools are there
   - Social Media
   - Apps
   - The knowledge economy

This brings me to the key question - Why Now?

I think it is one of those situations where everything is propitious for a revolution in dyslexia support.

The first wave has been completed. We have the awareness of disability, the legislation regarding disability, the representative bodies.

The science is right for the second phase. There have been great strides in Positive Psychology, Work Psychology, and Individual Psychology. Of course the genetics revolution is now going to mean that the psychology of individual differences dominates the next few years.

And finally, the tools are there - the social media, the apps, the knowledge economy.

Almost everything is in place - we are close to the tipping point.

1.8.3 Why you, the Reader?

> # Why You, the Reader !?
>
> 1. A movement builds from the grass-roots
> 2. Parents have the need and the determination to make a difference for the next generation
> 3. New technologies allow the combination of individual and social developments
> 4. The ideas I develop in this book are of direct value to everyone, young or old, dyslexic or not.
>
> There is much to be done!
> Together we can help dyslexics find and follow their stars!

So finally, why you, the reader?

We really do need you!

We cannot rely on the professionals to keep supporting dyslexic people in the way we want. They will do their best, but they march to a different drum.

And you have the numbers and the power...

- A movement builds from the grass-roots;
- Parents have the need and the determination to make a difference for the next generation;
- New technologies allow the combination of individual and social developments;
- The ideas I develop in this book are of direct value to everyone, young or old, dyslexic or not.

There is much to be done, but together we can help dyslexics find and follow their stars!

1.8.4 End of Chapter 1

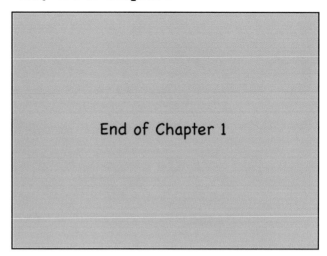

And that was the end of my talk and of Chapter 1.

I did in fact record the talk, and those of my co-presenters. Brock and Fernette Eide were kind enough to put the slides and the audio on Slideshare, where it could be accessed directly from their 'Dyslexic Advantage' website.

The talk received over 16,000 views over the next couple of years.

The movement is ready!

The remaining six chapters present my attempts to move on from this great beginning.

Chapter 2: Strengths of Dyslexia

2.1 Chapter Introduction

Positive Dyslexia

Chapter 2:
Strengths of Dyslexia

In Chapter 1 I presented the logic behind Positive Dyslexia - the need to work to strengths rather than weaknesses. Here I investigate what these strengths are, and come up with some very interesting findings.

2.1.1 The Positive Dyslexia Journey

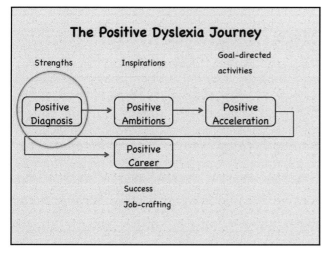

This is the blueprint I presented for the Dyslexia Journey in Chapter 1.

If we are indeed to diagnose strengths as well as weaknesses, we need to know what these characteristic strengths are!

2.1.2 Overview of Chapter 2

Overview of Chapter 2

1. Personal Best strengths not super strengths!
2. Dyslexia Hall of Fame
3. Strengths from the Literature
4. The Dyslexic Advantage MIND strengths
5. Sheffield Strengths Studies
   • The Strengths Decathlon!
6. Conclusions

Here is the plan of the chapter. I will start by reminding you that everyone - absolutely everyone - has their own personal best strengths. These are what we are trying to find and develop.

So don't be concerned when I go through this Dyslexia Hall of Fame. This is just to get an idea of people who have different strengths and can be inspiring role models.

After the Hall of Fame - which is notable for the diversity of strengths found, I go through the literature, reporting what previous strengths advocates have found. Of particular note is the MIND strengths framework developed by Brock and Fernette Eide in their outstanding book, the Dyslexic Advantage, together with Thomas West's brilliant book on the visuospatial strengths of outstanding dyslexic people.

These formed the basis for Sara Agahi's PhD in Sheffield, where she took a range of reasonably successful dyslexic adults, and completed in depth interviews to tease out their strengths - a key point is that the interviewees rarely realized what their own strengths actually were. This allowed us to outline a novel 'Strengths Decathlon' set of 10 strengths, which seem to us to represent the characteristic strengths of dyslexic adults.

Interestingly, we found that dyslexic people tend to keep developing their strengths well into adult work life.

2.2 The Dyslexia Hall of Fame

The Dyslexia Hall of Fame

I move on to the Hall of Fame. It is probably fair to say that not all of these famous people were definitively dyslexic, given that many lived at a time when dyslexia was little diagnosed.

But just look at the diversity of talents I am going to show here. I just list a range of famous people in various categories, then I will go through several in a bit more detail, especially those whom I have the privilege of meeting.

2.2.1 Actors and Entertainers.

Actors & Entertainers

1. Harry Anderson
2. Orlando Bloom
3. Harry Belafonte
4. Charley Boorman
5. Tom Cruise
6. Danny Glover
7. Whoopi Goldberg
8. Jerry Hall
9. Susan Hampshire
10. Kiera Knightley
11. Jay Leno
12. Christopher Lowell
13. Oliver Reed
14. Keanu Reeves.
15. Tom Smothers
16. Billy Bob Thornton
17. Vince Vaughn
18. Robin Williams
19. Henry Winkler
20. Loretta Young

Clearly dyslexia is not a complete barrier to acting, and if you look up the web sites of these actors and entertainers, you will see how they have managed to cope with the difficulties while developing their strengths. I will just list them - alphabetical order.

Harry Anderson, Orlando Bloom, Harry Belafonte, Charley Boorman, Tom Cruise, Danny Glover, Whoopi Goldberg, Jerry Hall, Susan Hampshire, Kiera Knightley, Jay Leno, Christopher Lowell, Oliver Reed, Keanu Reeves., Tom Smothers, Billy Bob Thornton, Vince Vaughn, Robin Williams, Henry Winkler, Loretta Young.

A pretty good cast there!

2.2.2 Artists, Designers and Architects

Artists, Designers, & Architects

1. Leonardo da Vinci
2. Ansel Adams, Photographer
3. David Bailey, Photographer
4. Chuck Close, 'heads'
5. Ignacio Gomez, Muralist
6. Tommy Hilfiger, Clothing Designer
7. Ian Marley, Contemporary Artist, South Africa
8. Pablo Picasso
9. Robert Rauschenberg, modernist art
10. Auguste Rodin
11. Bennett Strahan, abstract impressionist
12. Robert Toth (artist, sculptor)
13. Jørn Utzon (architect, Sydney Opera house)
14. Willard Wigan, micro sculptor

There is no shortage of dyslexic artists, and of course a strong representation in design and architecture. Leonardo's mirror writing makes him a plausible contender, and the remainder are authenticated:

Leonardo da Vinci, Ansel Adams, David Bailey, Chuck Close, who does the huge heads, Ignacio Gomez, Tommy Hilfiger, Ian Marley, Pablo Picasso, Robert Rauschenberg, Auguste Rodin, Bennett Strahan, Robert Toth, Jørn Utzon, Willard Wigan.

2.2.3 Scientists and Inventors

Inventors & Scientists

1. Ann Bancroft, Arctic Explorer
2. Alexander Graham Bell
3. John Britten, Motor bike designer
4. Pierre Curie, Physicist
5. Thomas Edison
6. Albert Einstein
7. Michael Faraday
8. Carol Greider, Molecular Biologist, awarded 2009 Nobel Prize in Medicine
9. Matthew H. Schneps, Astrophysicist
10. Jack Horner, Paleontologist
11. Dr. Peter Lovatt, psychologist and dancer
12. Dr. James Lovelock, inventor, Gaia
13. Paul MacCready "Engineer of the Century"
14. Archer Martin, Chemist (1952 Nobel Laureate)
15. John R. Skoyles, Brain Researcher

There is an equally distinguished list of scientists and inventors, though it has to be said that the evidence is shaky for the earlier generations!

Ann Bancroft was the first woman to reach the North Pole on foot and by sled. She was also the first woman to cross both polar ice caps to reach the North and South Poles, as well as the first woman to ski across Greenland.

And there was also Alexander Graham Bell, John Britten, who designed the motor bike in the figure, Pierre Curie, Thomas Edison, Albert Einstein, Michael Faraday, Carol Greider, Matt Schneps, Jack Horner, Peter Lovatt, James Lovelock, Paul MacCready, Archer Martin, John R. Skoyles.

2.2.4 Law and Justice

Others in the Hall of Fame

1. Law & Justice
   - David Boies, Attorney
   - Erin Brockovich, Investigator
   - Jeffrey H. Gallet, Judge
2. Military Heroes:
   - "Stonewall" Jackson.
   - George Patton
3. Musicians & Vocalists:
   - Cher
   - Brad Little, musicals
   - John Lennon
   - Nigel Kennedy, Violinist
   - Bob Weir, Grateful Dead Guitarist
4. Advocates
   - Kate Griggs
   - www.xtraordinarypeople.com/

We have David Boies, Erin Brockovich, Jeffrey Gallet.

2.2.5 Military heroes

Heroes include "Stonewall" Jackson and George Patton.

2.2.6 Musicians and Vocalists:

Cher, Brad Little, John Lennon, Nigel Kennedy, Bob Weir (shown in the figure).

2.2.7 Advocates

Kate Griggs has set up this amazing website xtraordinarypeople.com

I will now go through some more famous ones in more detail.

2.2.8 Pablo Picasso

Pablo Picasso

1. became an art icon despite, and no doubt because of, his apparent dyslexia.
2. failed parochial school education because of reading and related academic difficulties
3. encouraged by his father, an art teacher, to develop his obvious artistic talent.
4. Painted things as he saw or felt them — out of order, from all sides or tilted.

Pablo Picasso became an art icon despite, and no doubt because of, his apparent dyslexia. He failed parochial school education because of reading and related academic difficulties, and was encouraged by his father, an art teacher, to develop his obvious artistic talent.

And he created these amazing pictures, from left to right we have:

Garçon a la pipe in 1905, Les Demoiselles d'Avignon in 1907 - just two years later, Guernica in 1937 and Don Quixote in 1955.

He painted things as he saw or felt them - out of order, from all sides or tilted.

2.2.9 Steven Spielberg

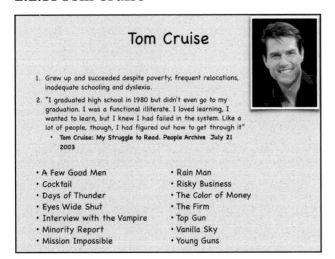

Steven Spielberg does not need much introduction to the modern generation - an extraordinarily popular and influential film director. Look at this set of films: Close Encounters of the Third Kind, E.T. The Extra-Terrestrial, Indiana Jones and the Temple of Doom, Jaws, Jurassic Park, Lincoln, Minority Report, Munich, Raiders of the Lost Ark, Saving Private Ryan, Schindler's List, and War of the Worlds.

He was diagnosed with dyslexia as late as 2007.

2.2.10 Tom Cruise

Tom Cruise grew up and succeeded despite poverty, frequent relocations, inadequate schooling and dyslexia.

"I graduated high school in 1980 but didn't even go to my graduation. I was a functional illiterate. I loved learning, I wanted to learn, but I knew I had failed in the system. Like a lot of people, though, I had figured out how to get through it" which is from 'The People Archive'.

His films include: A Few Good Men, Cocktail, Days of Thunder, Eyes Wide Shut, Interview with the Vampire, Minority Report, Mission Impossible, Rain Man, Risky Business, The Color of Money, The Firm, Top Gun, Vanilla Sky, and Young Guns.

Again, a stellar set of films.

2.2.11 Henry Winkler

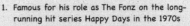
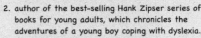

Henry Winkler was famous for his role as The Fonz on the long-running hit series Happy Days in the 1970s, but more recently he became the author of the best-selling Hank Zipzer series of books for young adults, which chronicles the adventures of a young boy coping with dyslexia [13].

A quote here from the Yale Center for Dyslexia and Creativity from Henry: "In addition to overcoming the struggles and the pain of being dyslexic, he also recognizes his strengths and gifts that come from it. Like his character, Hank, Henry is a problem solver. He can also see the big picture, and use it to help his friends. Like other dyslexics, he feels that 'sixth sense', that ability to sense things that are not said and really have a handle on who he is."

2.2.12 Sir Jackie Stewart

Sir Jackie Stewart
Formula 1 racing world champion 1969, 1971, 1973

1. "When you've got dyslexia and you find something you're good at, you put more into it than anyone else; you can't think the way of the clever folk, so you're always thinking out of the box."

2. "It has always seemed a paradox that I can't recite the alphabet beyond the letter "P", but I know every single gear change and braking distance required to negotiate the 187 corners around the 14.7-mile circuit at the old Nürburgring in Germany.

3. Then, in 1980, in a strange reversal of roles, I found myself cast as the concerned parent called to see the headmaster. This time the boy who was struggling with his academic work was our 12 year-old son, Mark. "Your son is dyslexic, which explains his difficulties at school," I was told. "How could he have got that?" "Well, it can be hereditary."

4. Twenty minutes later, after 41 years of feeling stupid and inferior, I too was diagnosed as dyslexic. It felt as if somebody was reaching out an arm and saving me from drowning. My sense of inadequacy was suddenly erased.

Now people I have met.

Jackie Stewart was Formula 1 world champion racing driver in 1969, 1971, and 1973. I had the privilege of hosting Jackie at the BDA 2001 Conference dinner. He had three words as the notes for his speech but gave a superb, coherent and moving account of his struggles with dyslexia. And despite - or because of - his dyslexia, he became the world Formula 1 racing champion, made an enormous contribution to Formula 1 safety, and went on to be a successful race team owner, consultant, and commentator.

Quotes from Jackie: [14]

"When you've got dyslexia and you find something you're good at, you put more into it than anyone else; you can't think the way of the clever folk, so you're always thinking out of the box."

"It has always seemed a paradox that I can't recite the alphabet beyond the letter 'P', but I know every single gear change and braking distance required to negotiate the 187 corners around the 14.7-mile circuit at the old Nürburgring in Germany.

Then, in 1980, in a strange reversal of roles, I found myself cast as the concerned parent called to see the headmaster. This time the boy who was struggling with his academic work was our 12 year-old son, Mark. "Your son is dyslexic, which explains his difficulties at school," I was told. "How could he have got that?" "Well, it can be hereditary."

Twenty minutes later, after 41 years of feeling stupid and inferior, I too was diagnosed as dyslexic. It felt as if somebody was reaching out an arm and saving me from drowning. My sense of inadequacy was suddenly erased."

2.2.13 Sir Steven Redgrave

Steve Redgrave

Won Olympic gold medals in men's rowing at five consecutive games from 1984 to 2000.

Inspired by American swimmer Mark Spitz who won 7 gold medals in the 1972 Munich Games.

"I was 10 at the time and I was inspired. I thought: 'Wouldn't it be great to win one'."

"I was not the brightest academically, but sports training taught me discipline. After an hour or so on the water after school I would come home and do my homework. Without sport, it could have gone either way for me".

"You have to enjoy it. People talk of the sacrifices but if I had my time all over again, I'd do it all again for half as good results".

Steven Redgrave is a British sporting icon. I had the pleasure of chatting with Sir Steve at the 2004 BDA conference. He is a shining example of the Positive Dyslexia journey - inspiration, determination and enjoyment - a man who has worked to his strengths and followed his star through grit and dedication. He won gold medals in men's rowing at five consecutive Olympic Games.

Sir Steve told youngsters [15] how he had been inspired by American swimmer Mark Spitz who became the first man to win seven gold medals at the same Olympics in the 1972 Games in Munich.

"I was 10 at the time and it made a tremendous impression on me," he said. "I was inspired. I thought: 'Wouldn't it be great to win one.'" ... The former rower, who is dyslexic, described his younger self as 'not the brightest tool in the box academically' and said sports training taught him discipline.

"After an hour or so on the water after school I would come home and do my homework. Without sport, it could have gone either way for me," he said.

But he added: "You have to enjoy it. People talk of the sacrifices but if I had my time all over again, I'd do it all again for half as good results.

2.2.14 Philip Schultz.

Philip Schultz: Poet

- Pulitzer Prize 2008
- 'My Dyslexia' 2011
- One called him a nobody.
  No, I said, he was a failure.
  You can't remember
  a nobody's name, that's why
  they're called nobodies.
  Failures are unforgettable.
  — from "Failure" 2007

2.2.15 Jack Laws

Jack Laws

1. Grew up in Yosemite. Naturalist, artist, best-selling author, wildlife educator, innovator
2. Developed new indexing method by visual characteristics (eg. all green birds) rather than taxonomic feature
3. Laws painted every wildflower in his book from sketches and paintings in the field. "We have this idea that all robins, for example, look the same," says Laws. "But they don't. Any more than all collies look alike or all humans. It's because we're not looking hard enough."

I had the pleasure of meeting Philip Schultz at the 2013 Dyslexia and Talent conference in Norwalk organized by Brock and Fernette Eide.

He has an international reputation as one of our most gifted poets - he was awarded the Pulitzer Prize in 2008 for his poetry.

He was diagnosed with dyslexia in much the same way as Jackie Stewart, when his son was diagnosed. This stimulated him to write the book 'My Dyslexia', published in 2011.

Phil gave a moving talk at Norwalk sharing the deep-seated insecurities that undermine even the most successful dyslexic adults - I'll quote directly: "It was a ceremony for the National Book Awards when I was young (about 30) and first came to New York. I was nominated and didn't win, and when the winner addressed the audience at Carnegie Hall he, referring to himself, said there was someone present who didn't belong there. Since that's what I felt, I was certain he was referring to me."

Here's a stanza from the title poem of the book that won him the Pulitzer [16]:

One called him a nobody.

No, I said, he was a failure.

You can't remember a nobody's name, that's why

they're called nobodies.

Failures are unforgettable.

- from "Failure" 2007

I also met Jack Laws in Norwalk, and bought his books to see how well they worked for me. His drawings are outstanding, and his organization - designed around the readers' interests rather than taxonomic principles - is completely intuitive. So he grew up in Yosemite. He's a naturalist, artist, best-selling author, wildlife educator, and innovator. He developed a new indexing method by visual characteristics (for instance, all green birds) rather than taxonomic features.

He painted every wildflower in his book from sketches and paintings in the field. "We have this idea that all robins, for example, look the same," says Laws. "But they don't. Any more than all collies look alike or all humans. It's because we're not looking hard enough." [17]

2.2.16 Jack Horner

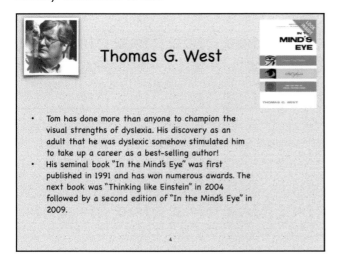

I shared a taxi with Jack Horner on the way back from the 2013 Dyslexia and Talent conference. He really has followed his star! He was fascinated from an early age by dinosaurs - he was born in Montana, and found his first dinosaur bone at 7 years...

Despite dyslexia, through cunning and determination he became a world famous dyslexia expert and is now Professor of Paleontology at the Museum of the Rockies. He was consultant to all the Jurassic Park films and is currently trying to build a dinosaur.

2.2.17 Thomas West

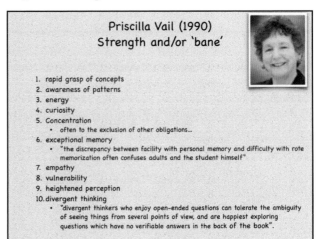

I have had the privilege of knowing Thomas West and his family for many years, even before he was diagnosed as dyslexic! He has done more than anyone to champion the visual strengths of dyslexia. His discovery as an adult that he was dyslexic

somehow stimulated him to take up a career as a best-selling author! His seminal book "In the Mind's Eye" was first published in 1991 and has won numerous awards. The next book was "Thinking like Einstein" in 2004 followed by a second edition of "In the Mind's Eye" in 2009 [18-20].

2.3 Are there typical strengths?

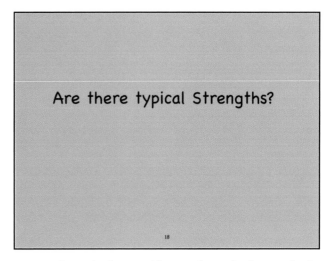

So, we have had a rapid run through the Dyslexia Hall of Fame. And it's a very impressive and diverse set of people with an impressive but diverse set of skills.

Is there any rationale for the skills dyslexic experts have? Are there typical strengths?

2.3.1 Strength or Bane!?

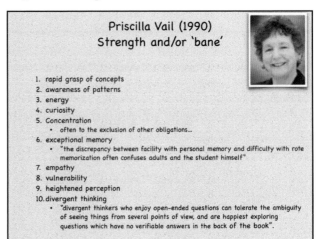

Priscilla Vail was one of the great dyslexia advocates, and accurately described it as a 'strength and / or a bane'. The key of course is to make it a strength, which is what Positive Dyslexia is all about. She put forward a series of 10 strengths: [21]

rapid grasp of concepts; awareness of patterns; energy; curiosity; Concentration - often to the exclusion of other obligations...; exceptional memory - "the discrepancy between facility with personal memory and difficulty with rote memorization often confuses adults and the student himself"; empathy; vulnerability; heightened perception; and divergent thinking - "divergent thinkers who enjoy open-ended questions can tolerate the ambiguity of seeing things from several points of view, and are happiest exploring questions which have no verifiable answers in the back of the book."

I think that's a very wise set of observations.

2.3.2 The Gift of Dyslexia

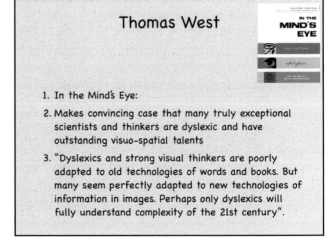

Ron Davis is dyslexic himself, and his book 'The Gift of Dyslexia' is a brilliant and inspiring personal statement. His approach to remediation has been harshly criticized by researchers from the mainstream reading tradition, but his understanding of the issues of dyslexia shines through [22].

In the book, Davis and Braun (1997) proposed eight 'gifts' of dyslexia:

the ability to alter and create perceptions (the primary ability); environmental sensitivity; curiosity; pictorial thinking; intuition and insight; multidimensional thought and perception (using all the senses); the ability to experience thought as reality; and a vivid imagination

"These eight basic abilities, if not suppressed, invalidated or destroyed by parents or the educational process, will result in two characteristics: higher-than-normal intelligence and extraordinary creative abilities. From these, the true gift of dyslexia will emerge - the gift of mastery."

2.3.3 In the Mind's Eye

I have already mentioned Thomas West in the context of a highly successful dyslexic author. But his books speak for themselves! "In the Mind's Eye" makes a convincing case that many truly exceptional scientists and thinkers are dyslexic and they have outstanding visuo-spatial talents.

"Dyslexics and strong visual thinkers are poorly adapted to old technologies of words and books. But many seem perfectly adapted to new technologies of information in images. Perhaps only dyslexics will fully understand complexity of the 21st century" [18].

2.3.4 The MIND Strengths

MIND Strengths in Dyslexia
Brock & Fernette Eide

- Material Reasoning
- Interconnected Reasoning
- Narrative Reasoning
- Dynamic Reasoning

The following slides about MIND strengths were presented by Brock Eide at the IDA 2012 conference and are included with the kind permission of Brock and Fernette Eide.

Finally, the brilliant and justly influential book by my friends Brock and Fernette Eide. The Dyslexic Advantage highlights the exceptional strengths of dyslexic people, creating the uplifting mnemonic of the MIND strengths [23] - which stands for:

M for Material Reasoning

I for Interconnected Reasoning

N for Narrative Reasoning, and

D for Dynamic Reasoning.

The following slides about MIND strengths were presented by Brock at the IDA 2012 conference and I am including them with the kind permission of Brock and Fernette Eide.

Material reasoning

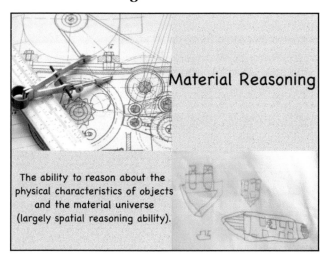

Material Reasoning

The ability to reason about the physical characteristics of objects and the material universe (largely spatial reasoning ability).

First comes Material Reasoning - The ability to reason about the physical characteristics of objects and the material universe, which is largely spatial reasoning ability.

On the top left we have the engineering drawings, and in the bottom right we have the 3D visualization ability of a very young dyslexic child.

Brock suggests that M skills are associated with affirmative answers to questions like:

- I am very good at forming 3D spatial images in my mind, and I can move them as I want to.
- I am good at understanding how machines work, and how their parts fit and act together.

Interconnected Reasoning

Interconnected Reasoning

1. The ability to spot connections or relationships between different objects, concepts, or points of view (similarity, causality, or correlation)
2. The ability to connect diverse perspectives (or see things from multiple points of view, often using approaches and techniques borrowed from other disciplines)
3. The ability to unite information into a single global or "big picture" perspective, and to determine large scale features like gist and context

Interconnected Reasoning is the ability to spot connections or relationships between different objects, concepts, or points of view (similarity, causality, or correlation). The ability to connect diverse perspectives (or see things from multiple points of view, often using approaches and techniques borrowed from other disciplines). And, third, the ability to unite information into a single global or 'big picture' perspective, and to determine large scale features like gist and context.

Brock suggests these types of questions in order to see whether you do have interconnected reasoning strengths:

- I often see connections and relationships that other people miss.
- I often spot things, needs, or ideas that are missing or lacking, or that aren't being recognized

- I often use analogies and metaphors to innovate new ideas, products, or procedures.

Narrative Reasoning

The ability to construct a connected series of mental scenes from past personal experience, to recall the past, understand the present, or create imaginary scenes.

Narrative Reasoning is the ability to construct a connected series of mental scenes from past personal experience, to recall the past, understand the present, or create imaginary scenes.

Brock suggests these sorts of questions:

- I enjoy creating and telling stories.
- When I think of concepts I usually think of cases or examples or mental 'scenes' rather than abstract verbal definitions.
- When I recall my past experiences my mind reconstructs the actual experience and I relive it again in my mind.

Dynamic Reasoning

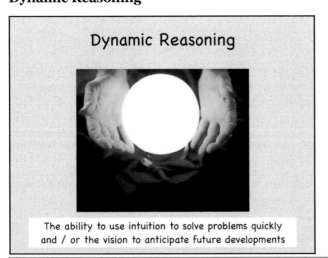

The ability to use intuition to solve problems quickly and / or the vision to anticipate future developments

Dynamic Reasoining is the ability to use intuition to solve problems quickly and / or the vision to anticipate future developments.

Brock suggests these sorts of questions:

- I have a good sense of 'vision' for where I think things are heading.
- I have a strong sense of intuition (or accurate hunches).
- I am comfortable working in situations where there are a lot of variables.

So those are the MIND strengths.

2.4 Recent Studies in Sheffield

Recent Studies in Sheffield

The above strengths literature informed the research program we have recently undertaken in Sheffield. In surveying the range of skills shown by dyslexic adults, we could see a lot of promising angles, but everyone seemed to have taken a different perspective, so there was a shortage of detailed evidence on which to build.

We did not know whether there were 'skill sub-types' so that some would show the M-skills but not the I-skills, some the I-skills but not the M-skills, or whether these skills tended to cluster together.

We also were not sure whether the successful dyslexics were somehow born with the skills - as seems to be the case with the extraordinary abilities reported by Tom West - or whether they developed through experience.

So we tried to find out... This was the start of Sara Agahi's PhD, starting in 2010 [24].

2.4.1 Strengths of Successful Dyslexic Adults

> ## Agahi and Nicolson study (2012)
>
> 1. In depth interviews with successful dyslexic adults in a range of careers
> 2. a salesman, a software analyst, an author, a lawyer, a doctor, an architect, a journalist, and a researcher
> 3. Structured interviews, Interpretative Phenomenological Analysis (qualitative)
> 4. Systematic methodology for extracting common themes

We deliberately chose reasonably successful (but not exceptionally successful) dyslexic adults, and deliberately chose a range of careers - there was a salesman, a software analyst, an author, a lawyer, a doctor, an architect, a journalist, and a researcher.

Sara undertook lengthy interviews - they all liked talking - and undertook detailed and systematic analyses of the rich data using the Interpretative Phenomenological Analysis which is a qualitative analysis method for systematically extracting common themes.

2.4.2 Themes Extracted

Six Specific and 3 integrative strengths		
Work Strengths	Cognitive Strengths	Inter-personal Strengths
Determination 87%	Big-Picture Approach 87%	Teamwork 62%
Resilience 75%	Innovation / Creativity 62%	Empathy 75%
Job Sampling 50%		
Flexible Coping, Preparation 100%		
Work Success Factors – Energy, Commitment 75%		

The power of the qualitative analysis methods is that it allows the strengths to emerge from the conversations even though it is worth noting that the dyslexic adults were not sure what their strengths were. the We classified the strengths in terms of three dimensions:

Work strengths (which is similar to the character strengths highlighted by positive psychologists, but in this case they are specifically those strengths which are valuable for work success).

The next dimension is cognitive strengths, which are essentially mental abilities, things you can do when thinking. These are the ones that were highlighted by previous research.

The third dimension is inter-personal, social, strengths, working with people.

The figure summarizes the findings:

Work Strengths - Determination, 87% (7 out of the 8 interviewees), Resilience, 75%.

Cognitive Strengths - the Big Picture approach (87%), Innovation and Creativity (62%).

The **inter-personal strengths** - Teamwork (62%) and Empathy (75%).

Underpinning all of these strengths, which we did not put in any category, we had Work Success factors - energy and commitment (75%); Flexible Coping and Preparation for meetings (100%), and Job Sampling (50%), that is having a variety of careers before settling down into the one that they preferred.

2.4.3 Strengths of Dyslexic Entrepreneurs

> ## Sepulveda, Agahi and Nicolson study (2013)
>
> 1. In depth interviews with 10 successful dyslexic entrepreneurs
> 2. Structured interviews, Interpretative Phenomenological Analysis (qualitative)
> 3. Systematic methodology for extracting common themes
> 4. Same methodology as Agahi study

Next, Poli Sepulveda undertook a similar set of interviews with dyslexic entrepreneurs, because it has been known since Julie Logan's studies that entrepreneurs seem to have a high incidence of dyslexia. And we chose people from the UK and Brazil and did a similar set of analyses for her Masters project.

So again, we undertook a similar sort of approach:

- In depth interviews with 10 successful dyslexic entrepreneurs;
- Structured interviews, Interpretative Phenomenological Analysis (qualitative);
- Systematic methodology for extracting common themes as in Sara's study.

Entrepreneur Strengths - Results

Entrepreneur Strengths		
Work Strengths	Entrepreneur Strengths	Inter-personal Strengths
Proactivity 80%	Vision 60%	Teamwork 70%
Resilience under Pressure 80%	{Innovation / Creativity}	Communication 90%
		Empathy 90%
Freedom! 100%		
Proactive Risk Management 90%		
Entrepreneur Family 100%		

And what we found is shown here, using a similar three dimensions of Work Strengths, Entrepreneur Strengths and Inter-personal Strengths:

Proactivity - thinking ahead to what you had to do

Resilience under pressure, so they were not phased by being under pressure.

Vision, Innovation and Creativity, which is implicit in entrepreneurs

And three inter-personal strengths: teamwork, communication and empathy again.

Underpinning those was the key idea of the entrepreneur family. It turned out all these entrepreneurs actually had an entrepreneurial family, and so had been exposed to the entrepreneurial approach all their life.

They also seemed to be particularly good at Proactive Risk Management - "what could possibly go wrong? What should I do to avoid that?"

And as all of them said, the Freedom to able to pursue their own star rather than be forced to work to someone else's tune.

2.4.4 Discussion of the Strengths findings

Study 2: Discussion

1. The entrepreneurs share some strengths found in Study 1
   - Work Strengths
     - Proactivity, Resilience, Coping Strategies, Work Success Factors
   - Cognitive and Inter-personal Strengths (The Big Six!)
     - Big Picture, Visuo-spatial, Creativity
     - Teamwork, Empathy, Communication
2. There are, however, entrepreneur-specific aspects:
   - Entrepreneur family
   - Risk (with precaution)
   - Freedom (with discipline)
3. We speculate that:
   - an entrepreneur with the necessary background skills and inclinations exploits the freedom and control of self-determination to thrive
   - For more conventional careers it takes longer to get to a role giving similar opportunities for self-determination

The findings of these studies indicate that:

The entrepreneurs share some strengths found by Sara:

In the Work Strengths we have: Proactivity, Resilience, Coping Strategies, and Work Success Factors which are pretty much the same

All six Cognitive and Inter-personal Strengths (The Big Six I've called them) also showed clear commonality:

- Big Picture, Visuo-spatial, Creativity;
- Teamwork, Empathy, Communication.

There are, however, entrepreneur-specific aspects:

- The Entrepreneur family, the willingness to take Risk (with precautions), and the idea of Freedom (with discipline).

We speculate that an entrepreneur with the necessary background skills and inclinations exploits the freedom and control of self-determination to thrive. But for more conventional careers it takes longer to get to a role giving similar opportunities for self-determination.

2.4.5 Thinking Skills and Dyslexia

Study 3: Thinking Skills and Dyslexia: Mumford and Nicolson (2014)

1. Piaget (1956) claimed that there are four general stages of cognitive development, ending with:
   - Concrete operational stage – reasoning about objects that are present
   - Formal operations stage – abstract thought
     - Deductive logic, problem solving, combining dimensions
2. Most adults do not fully acquire the formal operations abilities, with a reduction over the past decades in the % reaching FO from 1 in 4 in 1976 to 1 in 8 in 2007 (Shayer & Ginsburg, 2010).

I now move on to a third, more theoretical study, looking at thinking skills and dyslexia. This was undertaken by Sally Mumford in the course of her PhD, which was actually on personnel selection, and takes this more theoretical line.

We were interested to see whether dyslexic students did in fact appear to have somewhat better developed thinking skills than their non-dyslexic peers. I personally expected them to be better able to cope with uncertainty, to cope with problems with 'fuzzy' solutions, but we did not have time in Sally's PhD to do more than the first of a possible series of tests [25].

These were based on Jean Piaget's framework which claims that if a child is able to develop the ability to think in abstract terms (which he called 'formal operational thinking') then this causes a major leap in his or her intellectual performance all round. So it is a long-established framework.

Piaget suggested that there are four general stages of cognitive development, ending with:

- the Concrete operational stage - which is normally completed by the age of about 11 - the ability to reason about objects that are actually present.

- This is followed by the Formal operations stage - which is abstract thought, the ability to reason about objects that are not present. The key aspects of formal operations are deductive logic, problem solving, and the ability to combine different dimensions of a problem.

Interestingly, most adults do not fully acquire the formal operations abilities. Indeed in recent decades the numbers have actually gone down, with the percent reaching Formal Operations have fallen from 1 in 4 (25%) in 1976 to half that in 2007 (work by Michael Shayer).

Thinking skills: Method

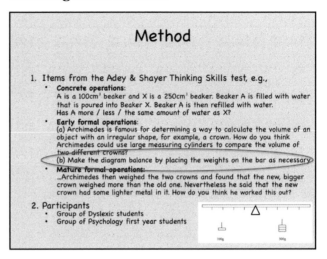

Method

1. Items from the Adey & Shayer Thinking Skills test, e.g.,
   - **Concrete operations:**
     A is a 100cm³ beaker and X is a 250cm³ beaker. Beaker A is filled with water that is poured into Beaker X. Beaker A is then refilled with water. Has A more / less / the same amount of water as X?
   - **Early formal operations:**
     (a) Archimedes is famous for determining a way to calculate the volume of an object with an irregular shape, for example, a crown. How do you think Archimedes could use large measuring cylinders to compare the volume of two different crowns?
     (b) Make the diagram balance by placing the weights on the bar as necessary
   - **Mature formal operations:**
     ...Archimedes then weighed the two crowns and found that the new, bigger crown weighed more than the old one. Nevertheless he said that the new crown had some lighter metal in it. How do you think he worked this out?
2. Participants
   - Group of Dyslexic students
   - Group of Psychology first year students

So that was our idea, here is our Method.

We took the items from the Adey and Shayer Thinking Skills test [26].

Here are some examples:

For Concrete operations, we have this deceptively difficult question:

- A is a 100cm³ beaker and X is a 250cm³ beaker. Beaker A is filled with water that is poured into Beaker X. Beaker A is then refilled with water. Has A more / less / the same amount of water as X?

This is more of a sort of a tongue-twister than anything else. It is actually a very easy problem if you can visualize what's going on. A has 100 cc and X has 100cc, so they are the same is the true answer.

Then the early formal operations:
(a) Archimedes is famous for determining a way to calculate the volume of an object with an irregular shape, for example, a crown. How do you think Archimedes could use large measuring cylinders to compare the volume of two different crowns?

Or - and this is the one with the illustration in the figure - Make the diagram balance by placing the weights on the bar as necessary.

The idea is that you have to put the lighter weight further away from the fulcrum than the heavier weight, because the moments of the weights have to balance. And that requires formal operations because you have to be able to visualize these things and then to combine different dimensions.

There is also Mature Formal Operations - continuing the Archimedes theme:

- ...Archimedes then weighed the two crowns and found that the new, bigger crown weighed more than the old one. Nevertheless he said that the new crown had some lighter metal in it. How do you think he worked this out?

So that is a more complex one still.

For participants we had a group of dyslexic University students and a group of first year University students studying Psychology.

And we compared their performance on these tasks.

Thinking Skills Results

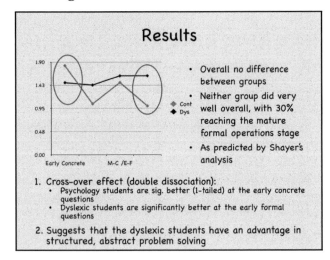

And this is what we found. Overall there was no difference between groups. Neither group did very well overall, with 30% reaching the mature formal operations stage, which is pretty much what you would expect predicted by Shayer's analysis of current performance [27].

But when we look at the actual performance, if you look at the controls, they were good on the early concrete and less good on the formal operations. Whereas the dyslexics were the other way round.

They were not good on that early concrete one, but they were actually pretty good on the more complex reasoning skills. In fact there was a significant interaction, moving from early concrete to the early formal operations stage.

From the perspective of Positive Dyslexia, these are really interesting findings, because that cross-over effect suggests that the dyslexic students have an advantage in structured, abstract problem solving. It does seem that the dyslexic students were relatively good at the high level thinking and relatively weak at the concrete, numerical reasoning.

This gives some justification for investigating these issues further, and in particular to see whether dyslexic adults are in fact better at the fuzzy reasoning under uncertainty that is thought to characterize the next stage up after formal reasoning.

2.4.6 Summary of the Sheffield Strengths Studies

Summary

1. There is insight but limitation in previous analyses:
   - each picks up an important characteristic
   - But each omits some perspective
2. Many of the strengths develop through experience
   - Resilience, determination and over-preparation arise from school failures
   - Teamwork and empathy may derive partly from need for support by others at school
   - Varied experience and lack of routine lead to wealth of experience which may support Big Picture and Creativity
   - The apparent advantage in high-level thinking merits further investigation
3. Exceptional talents in VisuoSpatial skill, exceptional memory and/or observation are rare even in dyslexic adults

In summary, these findings generally support but also enhance the previous analyses.

Many of the strengths do seem to develop through experience:

- Resilience, determination and over-preparation arise from school failures;
- Teamwork and empathy may derive partly from need for support by others at school;
- Varied experience and lack of routine lead to a wealth of experience which may well support Big Picture and Creativity;

The apparent advantage in high-level thinking skills merits further investigation.

On the other hand, exceptional talents in Visuo-Spatial skill, and exceptional memory and/or observation are rare even in dyslexic adults.

2.4.7 The Dyslexia Decathlon

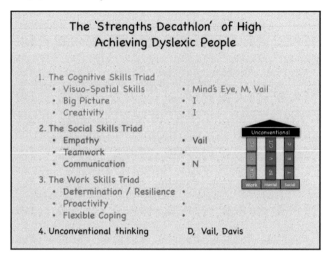

This Strengths Decathlon temple represents our take on the combined studies undertaken in Sheffield on successful dyslexics and on dyslexic entrepreneurs and dyslexic students. A key point here is that I have called it 'the Decathlon' - this is to indicate both the variety of skills and the fact that they are skills, which can - and must - be developed through practice - like the athletic decathlon.

There are three Strengths Triads:

- the Cognitive Skills Triad of Visuo-Spatial Skills, Big Picture and Creativity;
- the Social Skills Triad of Empathy, Teamwork and Communication;
- the Work Skills Triad of Determination / Resilience, Proactivity and Flexible Coping.

Underpinning all of these is what I have called Unconventional Thinking, which is a slight broadening of the category as a consequence of Sally's findings - and the strong evidence throughout the literature on the way that dyslexic people do seem to think differently.

I return to this issue in Chapter 3, where I consider the relevant theoretical interpretations.

Let us consider how these compare with the studies I have mentioned earlier. So:

- Cognitive skills:

- Visuo-Spatial skills, certainly the Mind's eye, M for Material Reasoning and in Priscilla Vail's analysis.
- The Big Picture, I for Interconnected Reasoning.
- Creativity, the Mind's eye, and also I for Interconnected Reasoning.
- Social Skills
  - Empathy, yes for Vail.
  - Teamwork, missing from most of the literature.
  - Communication, N for Narrative Reasoning.
- Work Skills
  - do not seem to have been highlighted previously. Possibly because they are work skills that develop relatively late on, or perhaps because they are not conventionally thought of as talents.
- Then the Unconventional Thinking:
  - Here we have the D for Dynamic Reasoning, also Priscilla Vail and Ron Davis highlight these skills.

Our findings indicate that the majority of the dyslexic participants showed strengths in the majority of these ten skills, but especially so with the cognitive triad and the social triad. These compare quite interestingly with the existing literature, and I will return to these strengths repeatedly throughout the book.

2.5 Conclusions on Strengths

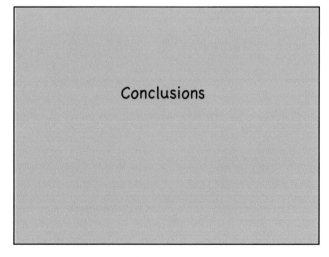

In summary, I have done a rapid run through of the Dyslexia Hall of Fame, which gives an intriguing picture of the diversity of strengths in dyslexia. I have also surveyed the published literature on strengths, and reported a series of studies we have undertaken recently in Sheffield.

2.5.1 Conclusions to Chapter 2

> ## Conclusions to Chapter 2
>
> 1. There is no doubt - as testified by the Dyslexia Hall of Fame - that it is possible to be highly successful as a dyslexic adult, in many ways and many careers
>
> 2. The classification which we derived on the basis of literature reviews and recent work in Sheffield is the 'Dyslexia Decathlon'. This characterised the strengths into three 'triads' - Work Strengths, Cognitive Strengths, and Social Strengths, all underpinned by 'Unconventional Thinking' strengths
>
> 3. Extraordinary talents are the exception rather than the rule even in dyslexia, but strengths in dyslexia tend to emerge after the school years. These 'learned talents' may keep developing, often through the variety of experiences gained
>
> 4. There are large individual differences arising from variations in experience and in talent. It is therefore critical to take an individual approach
>
> 5. Nonetheless, there is sufficient overlap between many of the core strengths that it is appropriate to consider a 'syndrome of strengths' and to tailor diagnostic and support systems to this set.

It is time to Conclude! The conclusions are very positive. There is no doubt - as testified by the Dyslexia Hall of Fame - that it is possible to be highly successful as a dyslexic adult, in many ways and many careers.

The classification which we derived on the basis of literature reviews and recent work in Sheffield is the 'Dyslexia Decathlon'. This classifies the strengths into three 'triads' - Work Strengths, Cognitive Strengths, and Social Strengths, all underpinned by 'Unconventional Thinking' strengths.

Extraordinary talents are the exception rather than the rule even in dyslexia, but strengths in dyslexia tend to emerge after the school years. These 'learned talents' may keep developing, often through the variety of experiences gained.

There are large individual differences arising from variations in experience and in talent. It is therefore critical to take an individual approach.

Nonetheless, there is sufficient overlap between many of the core strengths that it is appropriate to consider a 'syndrome of strengths' and to tailor diagnostic and support systems to this set.

So everything is there to play for in the following chapters!

2.6 End of Chapter 2

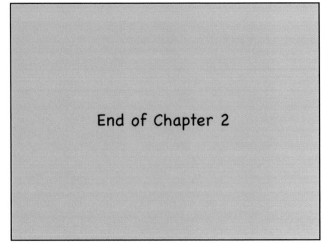

This has been an empirical chapter, trying to gather the evidence needed to decide what strengths are characteristic of dyslexia.

The results were exciting, strongly supporting the goals of Positive Dyslexia - there are characteristic strengths, but most of them can be further developed through experience or appropriate training!

Chapter 3 follows this up by investigating the key theoretical question - why do dyslexic people have these strengths!?

Chapter 3: Why Dyslexia?

3.1 Chapter Introduction

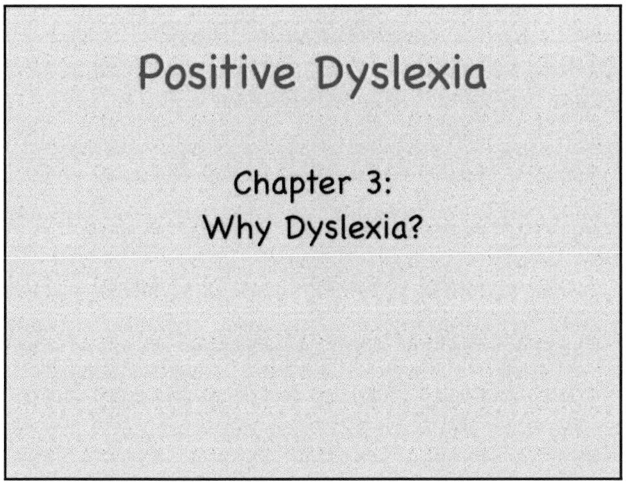

> ## Positive Dyslexia
>
> ### Chapter 3:
> ### Why Dyslexia?

In Chapter 1 I presented the logic behind Positive Dyslexia, the need to work to strengths rather than weaknesses. In Chapter 2 I presented an empirical survey of the strengths of dyslexia.

But the question is - why do some dyslexic people show these strengths?

And for that we need to move from describing to explaining - we need some theory. And at last I believe we have a theoretical framework with the power to explain both deficits and strengths, from pre-school to adulthood.

3.1.1 Dyslexia: the Key Conundrum

> **Dyslexia: The Key Conundrum**
> If dyslexic children cannot learn the way we teach, we must teach them the way they learn
>
> 1. How do dyslexic children learn?
>
> 2. How should we teach them?
>
> To answer these questions we need a theoretical understanding of the cause(s) of dyslexia

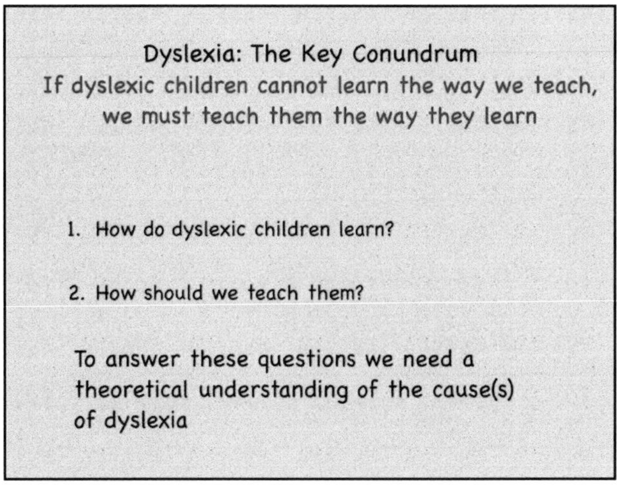

You will be familiar with this inspirational mantra,

"If dyslexic children cannot learn the way we teach, we must teach them the way they learn."

It leads to these two issues that I raised back in 2001 in my Keynote address to the BDA International Conference:

- how do dyslexic children learn?
- how should we teach them?

And this is why I have to take a detour to go through theories of dyslexia. It is is also where I part company with Reading Disability research over the past 30 years. Reading Disability researchers have taken the view (following Frank Vellutino) that it is more important to look at the teaching of reading than the learning processes.

Positive Psychology says that you must look from the perspective of the learner, not of the teacher. And so I consider learning in this chapter, and teaching in the next one.

The learning framework is of great power, and I think, at last, I have a set of answers! But it is a challenging chapter, and can be skimmed if you prefer.

In order to answer these questions we need a theoretical understanding of the causes of dyslexia.

3.1.2 Acknowledgment: Angela Fawcett

Acknowledgment:
Angela Fawcett

- Angela is an inspiring advocate for dyslexic people, showing how a parent can make a real difference not just to their own child but to the dyslexia community.
- Undertook a Psychology degree then PhD to better understand the causes of dyslexia
- Coauthor with me of 3 major theories and 4 screening tests, and with strong international profile.
- She is Professor Emeritus at Swansea University, a Vice-President of the British Dyslexia Association and was for a decade the Editor of the journal Dyslexia.

First I must gratefully acknowledge the contributions of my collaborator in most of this work, Angela Fawcett. Angela is an inspiring advocate for dyslexic people. Seeing the problems caused by lack of understanding of dyslexia at first hand, as a wife and parent, she decided to do something about it!

While raising her family she took a degree in Psychology at the University of Sheffield, and she then dragged me in to supervise her PhD 25 years ago.

We were fortunate to make some early breakthroughs, and she has never looked back. Angela is coauthor with me of 3 major theories, 4 screening tests, the book 'Dyslexia: Learning and the Brain' and she has a strong international research and practice profile [28].

Angela is Professor Emeritus at Swansea University, a Vice-President of the British Dyslexia Association and was for a decade the Editor of the journal Dyslexia, taking over from Tim Miles.

3.1.3 Plan of Chapter 3

Plan of Chapter

1. Causal Theories of Dyslexia
   - Phonological Deficit
2. Learning to read: what is needed?
3. Mind-based vs brain-based learning
4. Procedural Deficit vs Declarative Advantage
5. The Delayed Neural Commitment Hypothesis
6. Why Strengths!?

The plan of the chapter is as follows.

- First, Causal Theories of Dyslexia where I go through the Phonological Deficit - the leading theory.
- Then Learning to read: what is needed.
- Mind-based vs brain-based learning.
- Procedural Deficit vs Declarative Advantage.
- And then the Delayed Neural Commitment Hypothesis, which I believe is the integrative framework we need.

And I can then get back to "why are there strengths?"

3.1.4 The Target Causal Analysis

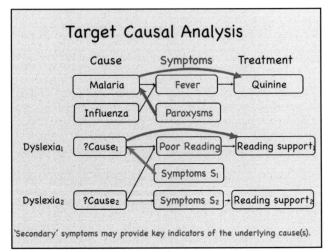

This figure indicates why I have parted company with so many excellent dyslexia researchers in the approach I have taken. I think it is crucial to

understanding scientific approaches to theory development

Imagine that you are a tropical doctor and a patient comes to you with a fever. You think it is likely to be malaria - what do you do?

The traditional medical model distinguishes clearly between symptoms, cause and treatment. Meningitis or flu have similar symptoms of fever (and headache), but of course the causes and treatments are entirely different.

So before you treat, you find the cause - you need to identify secondary symptoms. For malaria, the secondary symptoms are things like profuse sweating and paroxysms. Taken in conjunction with the symptoms of fever and headache, these allow us to diagnose the underlying cause - malaria - and so give the appropriate treatment. So the secondary symptoms are just as important as the primary ones in making an accurate diagnosis.

Now consider dyslexia. There is at least one underlying (but unknown) cause - I have called it Cause 1. And there will be some associated reading support method with Cause 1 - Reading Support 1. And presumably it will have some secondary symptoms - S1.

But let's say there are two possible causes. So there is now another potential cause - Cause 2. Which again of course leads to poor reading, but will have different secondary symptoms - S2. And will have different reading support methods - Reading Support 2.

We therefore then look for the secondary symptoms. If we find secondary symptoms S1, that leads to the diagnosis of Cause 1, and therefore Reading Support 1. If it had been S2 we would have gone for Cause 2 and Reading Support 2.

I hope that this analysis indicates how crucial it is to look for secondary causes as well as primary ones. If all you look at is reading, you may never be able to start this analysis.

In summary, in order to make the right intervention we need to know the underlying cause of the child's problems, and for this we need a theory of the cause.

3.1.5 Deficit Theories of Dyslexia

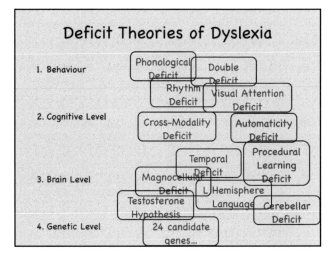

And there are many theories for the causes of Dyslexia! The focus of much of the research and advocacy for dyslexia over the past 30 years has been to establish dyslexia as a disability - this of course has led to major progress, and has led to a range of important theories from many eminent researchers internationally.

When talking about theories it is useful to distinguish three levels of explanation: behavior (which you can observe directly, like reading accuracy), the cognitive level (which gives a description of how the brain works overall for things like memory, language, and learning) and the brain level (which looks at the components of the brain). And these days there is also the genetic level.

In terms of theories, at the behavioral level, the problem is reading. The dominant theory for the cause of the reading problems is a cognitive level theory, phonological deficit, but there are actually many other cognitive level theories, some narrower, some broader.

The chart lists double deficit [29], rhythm deficit [30], visual attention deficit [31], cross-modality deficit [32], automaticity deficit [33], temporal deficit [34] and procedural learning deficit [35].

And at the brain level, theories include magnocellular deficit [36], left hemisphere language deficit, the testosterone hypothesis [37], and cerebellar deficit [38].

And at the genetic level there is a whole range of possible candidate genes, 24 have been established so far, though the consensus is that no single genes or set of genes is sufficient to explain the range of issues.

3.1.6 The Phonological Deficit Hypothesis

The Phonological Deficit Hypothesis

The reading difficulties are attributable to problems in phonological processing, that is breaking a word down into its constituent sounds. These difficulties cause problems in sound segmentation and also in word blending, both of which are critical for development of reading and spelling.

Lundberg, Olofsson & Wall (1980); Bradley and Bryant (1983), Lundberg & Høien (1989)
- Kindergarten children with poor phonological awareness later develop reading difficulties
- Support [specifically] with phonological awareness at kindergarten reduces the subsequent reading difficulties

Stanovich (1988). 'Phonological core, variable difference' model
  - one key to fluent reading is the development of an autonomously functioning module at the word recognition level ... failure to develop such a module may derive from impairments in phonological processing

I will move on to the Phonological Deficit Hypothesis. This has dominated the field for 30 years. And it is the only one I am able to give much space for in this book apart from my own theories. Anyone with an interest in more detail - and who likes an academic book with a strong narrative - might try my book with Angela Fawcett, Dyslexia Learning and the Brain [28].

The Phonological Deficit Hypothesis proposes that the reading difficulties are attributable to problems in phonological processing, that is breaking a word down into its constituent sounds. These difficulties cause problems in sound segmentation and also in word blending, both of which are critical for the development of reading and spelling. So for instance, breaking the word 'constituent' down into syllables, 'con-sti-tu-ent'. And then into the corresponding phonemes, 'cuh-oh-neh' etc.

This was inspired by work in the late 1970s and early 1980s by Frank Vellutino and by Ingvar Lundberg, and in the UK Lynette Bradley and Peter Bryant [39-41].

The basic finding was that kindergarten children with poor phonological awareness later develop reading difficulties, and support - specifically with phonological awareness - at kindergarten reduces the subsequent reading difficulties.

Keith Stanovich gave the clearest description of the theory, in terms of his 'Phonological core, variable difference' model. The key idea is that all dyslexic children will show a core problem in phonology, but will show differences in various other aspects - like motor skills, or speed of processing [42].

Stanovich's central point was that a 'key to fluent reading is the development of an autonomously functioning module at the word recognition level ... failure to develop such a module may derive from impairments in phonological processing.'

Consequently, the cause of the failure to develop fluent reading, sight-word reading, was actually earlier on with phonological difficulties.

Unresolved Issues for the Phonological Deficit Hypothesis

Unresolved issues for P.D.H

1. Diagnosis
   - Phonological skills are learned, or, failing that, may be taught
   - following appropriate support, a dyslexic child should be able to overcome his/her phonological and reading difficulties to the extent that he/she is no longer diagnosable as dyslexic.

2. Theory
   - Slow learners show equal or greater phonological difficulties. This has led some researchers (Shaywitz, Stanovich) to argue that distinction between the two groups is counter-productive.
   - What causes the phonological deficits!?

3. Scope
   - Relevant primarily for age 5-8 but not later
   - no strengths

4. My view
   - Reasonable description of the early reading-related difficulties
   - Doesn't explain the range of difficulties
   - A QWERTY theory

There are serious unresolved issues for the Phonological Deficit Hypothesis to the extent that I do have quite severe doubts as to its continuing value as a theory. As do most contemporary dyslexia theorists.

First, consider diagnosis. Phonological skills are learned, or, failing that, may be taught. There is not an absolute deficit, more like two years delay, so the diagnostic method has to be pretty sophisticated and carefully tailored to the age, and the country. Furthermore, following appropriate support, a dyslexic child can completely overcome his/her phonological difficulties. This would mean that according to the PDH he or she is no longer dyslexic. Which is inconsistent with the established view that dyslexia is a brain-based difference.

Next, there are serious problems in scope. Basically the PDH is relevant for the ages of about 4-8 years, but not for later, and certainly not in adulthood. And of course from my perspective, it does not talk about strengths at all. It has no explanation of strengths.

In terms of theory, one of the key difficulties is that slow learners - that is children without any discrepancy between their reading and other performance - show equal or greater phonological difficulties. And this has led some researchers - primarily in the United States - to argue that the distinction between the two groups is counter-productive.

But the most glaring theoretical weakness is in terms of explanation. What is it that causes the phonological deficits!? The Phonological Deficit Hypothesis is silent on this key issue.

You may be familiar with the QWERTY phenomenon. This refers to the fact that we still have keyboards with QWERTY keys in the top left. This layout was actually designed for the first typewriters to keep common pairs of letters apart so as to avoid the key levers jamming together! Because so many people used it for the careers, and there was no consensus as to how to replace it, the QWERTY keyboard has lingered on despite its obvious inadequacies. My view, is that the PDH is certainly a reasonable description of the early reading-related difficulties but it does not explain the range of difficulties and is in fact a QWERTY theory, lingering on long past its sell-by date.

3.2 Reading: What Develops?

Reading: What Develops?

One of the weaknesses of the PDH is that it is not a developmental theory - it does not consider what happens as one learns to read. One of the results of

the revolution in cognitive neuroscience that has happened in the past 30 years since the PDH was proposed is that we now have a much better understanding of the brain circuitry changes that are involved. So we now know much better what does develop as a child learns to read.

3.2.1 Mature Reading Circuits

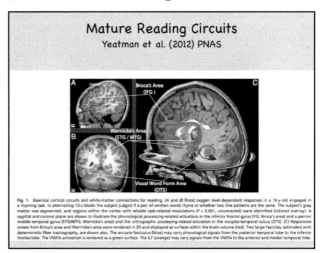

Fig. 1. Essential cortical circuits and white-matter connections for reading. (A and B) Blood oxygen level-dependent responses in a 10-y-old engaged in a rhyming task. In alternating 12-s blocks the subject judged if a pair of written words rhyme or whether two line patterns are the same. The subject's gray matter was segmented, and regions within the cortex with reliable task-related modulations (P < 0.001, uncorrected) were identified (colored overlay). A sagittal and coronal plane are shown to illustrate the phonological processing-related activations in the inferior frontal gyrus (IFG; Broca's area) and superior/ middle temporal gyrus (STG/MTG; Wernicke's area) and the orthographic processing-related activation in the occipito-temporal sulcus (OTS). (C) Responsive voxels from Broca's area and Wernicke's area were rendered in 3D and displayed as surfaces within the brain volume (red). Two large fascicles, estimated with deterministic fiber tractography, are shown also. The arcuate fasciculus (blue) may carry phonological signals from the posterior temporal lobe to the inferior frontal lobe. The VWFA activation is rendered as a green surface. The ILF (orange) may carry signals from the VWFA to the anterior and medial temporal lobe.

This lovely picture, from Jason Yeatman and his colleagues, shows combined DTI - diffusion tensor imaging - data which allows you to work out what the neural tracts are. It combines that with functional imaging data for a 10 year old child doing a rhyming task and it allows us to see the neural circuits involved in reading. The left hand panel is to do with the functional imaging, and the right hand panel is to do with the underlying circuitry. You see it is a fascinating picture [43].

The green area is known as the 'Visual Word Form Area' and because it's close to the visual cortex, it allows very rapid sight word reading. It develops through experience and expertise, and connects to the previous reading circuits for meaning, spelling, phonology and articulation.

The blue tract is the arcuate fasciculus and connects Broca's area, which is the speech area, with Wernicke's area - the hearing speech area - and the Visual Word Form Area.

The orange tract is the inferior longitudinal fasciculus, and probably connects to the semantic areas in the temporal lobe.

The important thing though, is that the brain builds these circuits through the experience of reading. They are not there at 4 years, and they do not develop without fluent reading.

3.2.2 What needs to happen for fluent reading?

What needs to happen for fluent reading

- Automatize sub-skills
  - Letters
  - Grapheme-to-phoneme
  - Orthography
  - Word fixation
  - Speech internalization
- Co-ordinate sub-skills
  - Predictive eye movements
  - Eye-voice span
  - Lexical look-up
- Build and rebuild the necessary neural circuits
  - Phonological circuit
  - Visual Word Form Area
  - Circuit building
  - Circuit coordination
  - Circuit myelination

Having seen the circuits that can develop, we are now in position to specify what needs to happen for fluent reading.

In order to read fluently you need to be able to:

(1) automatize the sub-skills, the letters, the grapheme-to-phoneme (that's the visual form to the sounds of the letters), the orthography (that's the spelling), the word fixation (that's the ability to focus on just one word or just one letter within that word), speech internalization (to be able to say the words in your head without saying them out loud).

(2) You need to be able to co-ordinate these sub-skills. You need to be able to make predictive eye movements so that your eyes are ahead of your voice. You have an eye-voice span. You need a lexical look-up so that you automatically look-up what the meaning of each word that you read is.

And (3), you need to build and rebuild the necessary neural circuits. You need to build the Phonological circuit. You need to build the Visual Word Form Area. You need to build those circuits, you need to coordinate those circuits, you need to myelinate those circuits, so that they work more effectively.

All that needs to happen for fluent reading. For reasons more related to the politics of reading research than the appliance of science, dyslexia researchers have focused on a very small subset of

these processes - specifically the first three in (1) and the first two in (3).

3.3 Nicolson and Fawcett Research Phase 1: Dyslexia and Learning

Nicolson and Fawcett Theory
Dyslexia and Learning
Phase 1: 1988-1995

In my research with Angela Fawcett during her PhD we deliberately took a contrarian view - what is it that the other researchers are NOT doing. Given the absence of dyslexia funding in the UK, that appeared to us to be the most productive approach.

My expertise is in human learning, and I was convinced that any solution must involve analysis of the underlying learning differences in dyslexia.

3.3.1 The Dyslexic Automatization Deficit hypothesis

Dyslexia as a Learning Disability:
The Automatization Deficit Hypothesis

The 'correct' description of dyslexia is 'Specific Learning Difficulties' or '{Specific} Learning Disability'

Dyslexia is [some] general deficit in learning
- For some reason it is difficult for dyslexic children to become 'expert' in a task
- ....whether it is a cognitive task or a motor task.

The Automatization Deficit hypothesis (N & F 1990)
- Dyslexic children have problems making skills automatic and need therefore to 'consciously compensate' even for simple skills

Our bland general hypothesis was that there is some problem somewhere in the learning processes. Given that in the UK the 'correct' description of dyslexia is 'Specific Learning Difficulties' and in the US 'Specific Learning Disability', it hardly should have been too controversial, and it led us to the idea that dyslexia is some general deficit in learning and for some reason it is difficult for dyslexic children to become 'expert' in a task [33].

Given the commonality between motor learning and cognitive learning, we proposed the strong form of the hypothesis that the problems should be evident in both types, whether the task is a cognitive task or a motor task.

And this led us to the Dyslexic Automatization Deficit hypothesis, that dyslexic children have problems making skills automatic and need to 'consciously compensate' even for simple skills.

So if a task is not too difficult, dyslexic children might well be able to perform within the normal range, but they would be doing it by explicitly concentrating hard on it, whereas a non-dyslexic child would just 'download' the task to some unconscious automatic mechanism.

I see it a bit like listening to someone speaking with an unusual accent - you can follow it, but need to concentrate hard. Or like driving in a foreign country. Unfortunately, for a dyslexic child, there is no 'home' accent and no 'home country'.

This hypothesis was very warmly welcomed by large numbers of dyslexic individuals, who all said that seemed to capture their difficulties extremely well. As Tim Miles said, we got the "That's my Johnny" response.

But of course we needed to do the science.

3.3.2 Our research on Dyslexia and Learning

> ### Nicolson & Fawcett Theory
> ### Phase 1 (1988-1995)
>
> Logic
> - Reading-related tests do not discriminate between the theories
> - What is needed is a test in a domain where some theories predict no deficit - this is Popper's falsification approach.
>
> We tested their motor skills. They were worse than normal - even for the highly practised skill of balance!

The logic behind the science was as follows: reading-related tests do not discriminate between the theories, so what is needed is a test in a domain where some theories predict no deficit - this is Popper's falsification approach.

This was again a departure from established wisdom in the field. For many researchers into reading disability it seemed frankly crazy to look outside of the reading domain when trying to find the cause of reading disability.

I must admit I have never seen anything special about reading, myself. It is not wired into the brain like language, there is no special reading-acquisition-device in our heads. Historically there have been many illiterate societies.

In my view the processes of learning to read are similar to the processes of learning to play chess, or learning to drive - a combination of cognitive and physical skills that are slowly built up by experience.

So for me it made perfect sense to look outside the reading box - indeed it seemed to me to be completely against scientific principles NOT to!

Consequently, we tested their motor skills. And Angela found that they were worse than normal - even for the highly practiced skill of balance!

3.3.3 Study 1: Balance and Dyslexia

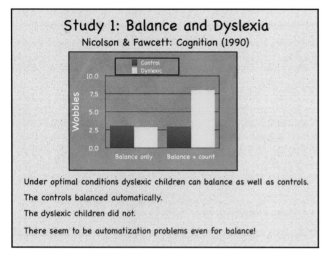

Study 1: Balance and Dyslexia
Nicolson & Fawcett: Cognition (1990)

Under optimal conditions dyslexic children can balance as well as controls.

The controls balanced automatically.

The dyslexic children did not.

There seem to be automatization problems even for balance!

This was our key study on balance. We took balance because it was the motor skill that everyone has practiced endlessly and for which there was solid evidence - in 1989 when we started - that dyslexic children over the age of 9 do not have balance problems. We used the 'one foot in front of the other' Romberg task, which assesses side-to-side balance. The particpants were 13 year old dyslexic and control adolescents matched for IQ and age.

We asked them to balance for 30 seconds and we measured the number of wobbles. There were two conditions, one where they just balanced and one where they balanced and counted at the same time. It turned out we had to make the counting task individually calibrated so that it was equally easy for each person. So for some of our dyslexic participants, they were counting forwards from 10 in ones, whereas most of our controls were counting backwards from 100 in 3s (100, 97, 94...).

So what did we find? For the single task condition, just standing there balancing, there was no difference between the two groups. They made very few wobbles, they were pretty solid. That was as predicted from the literature.

But when we looked at the dual task - where they had to balance and count - the chart shows that the control participants were not affected at all on the balance, whereas the dyslexic participants clearly wobbled a lot more.

So under optimal conditions, dyslexic children can balance as well as controls. But the controls were balancing automatically, whereas the dyslexic

children were not. There seemed to be automatization problems even for balance.

We also checked these results with different balance tasks, including a blindfold balance task, designed to make sure that participants could not visually compensate for any balance problems. We got the same results [44].

So that seemed to be very strong evidence for an automatization deficit account. And of course it was completely contrary to the predictions of the Phonological Deficit Hypothesis.

3.3.4 Study 2: Blending of procedural skills

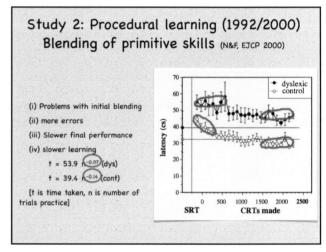

Study 2: Procedural learning (1992/2000)
Blending of primitive skills (N&F, EJCP 2000)

(i) Problems with initial blending
(ii) more errors
(iii) Slower final performance
(iv) slower learning

$t = 53.9 \ n^{-0.07}$ (dys)

$t = 39.4 \ n^{-0.14}$ (cont)

[t is time taken, n is number of trials practice]

The next study I present was actually a very simple one, in terms of blending procedural skills. It was published in 2000, although it was undertaken in 1992. It is one of the few direct tests of learning in the literature, and we obtained stunning results [45].

For scientific clarity we needed a skill away from reading or phonology, and we hit on the issue of skill blending. In a previous set of studies we had found that dyslexic children performed within the normal range on simple reactions [as soon as you hear the tone, you press the button as fast as you can] but that they were significantly slower on a choice reaction [if you hear the tone press the button, if you see the flash stamp on the foot button].

We decided to train our participants on this novel choice reaction task and monitor what happens in terms of the learning curves. We measured the latency, the time to make the response - shown in the figure in centiseconds, hundredths of a second. First we had the simple reaction time task. It can be seen (on the far left hand side of the chart) that the dyslexic participants were a bit slower but not significantly slower than the controls on the simple reaction task.

And then we changed to the choice reaction task. Both sets of participants were slower on the choice reaction than on the simple reaction - as one would expect. Interestingly, the dyslexic children were ijn fact more adversely affected.

However, our key question was, how about the learning? You can see we had 2500 trials which we took in repeated sessions over the next four weeks.

If we look at the controls, in blue, it is clear that their performance got steadily faster, it got better. So that by the end, in fact, their performance is better than it was even on the simple reactions.

For the dyslexics, we did not get such an effect, there was much less of a learning effect. Inspection of that first set of learning indicates that the controls learned rapidly over the first set of 100 trials or so, whereas the dyslexics appear to make no progress. And when one looks at the asymptote - the performance after many trials - the controls were actually better than their simple reactions whereas the dyslexic children were worse.

So to summarize: the dyslexic group showed problems with the initial blending of the two responses into one. They did make more errors (not shown on this chart) and they had slower final performance.

Crucially, they had slower learning. In fact, learning rate can be modeled using the power law, which shows that the time taken in the case of dyslexics was 53.9 multiplied by n (the number of trials) to the power -0.07, with similar numbers for the control group. t is the time taken, n is the number of trials practice.

The difference between -0.07 for the dyslexics compared with -0.14 for the controls in the learning exponent is of major significance, as I show in the next figure.

3.3.4.1 The difficulties lie at the start, the middle, the end and the blend!

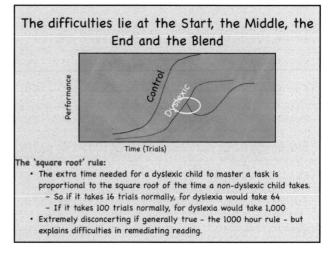

The above chart is intended to highlight where learning differences might occur. The curve labeled Control provides a standard learning curve, in which I have shown performance getting better as you go up. So learning typically starts slowly, then improves sharply, then ends at asymptote.

For the dyslexics, they started lower, they had a shallower learning curve (they learned slower) and they ended up asymptoted at a lower level. So the difficulties lay at the start, and the middle, and the end. And in fact difficulties also occurred when they had to blend skills together. For the dyslexic participants it was harder to blend two skills to make a new one. This is directly as predicted from conscious compensation, in that it is impossible to consciously compensate two skills simultaneously.

Now it is important to note the power of the mathematical modeling we did. Because it allowed us to derive what I have called the 'square root' rule. It allows one to predict how much longer it will take a dyslexic child to learn something than a non-dyslexic child. And it turns out that the 'square root' rule tells us that the difference depends on how hard the task is. The extra time needed for a dyslexic child to master a task, is proportional to the square root of the time a non-dyslexic child takes.

It is hard to grasp what that means, but if it takes 16 trials normally, it would take 4 (which is the square root of 16) times 16 which is 64. For a dyslexic child it would take 4 times as long. If it takes 100 trials normally, for a dyslexic child it would 10 times as long, that is a 1000 trials. This is extremely disconcerting if generally true - for instance expert skills generally take 1000 hours to develop, and if something takes 1000 trials to develop the square root of 1000 is about 31, and so it would take a dyslexic child 31,000 hours to develop that. And this explains the difficulties in remediating reading.

It is therefore no surprise that even with exemplary support, dyslexic children have difficulty mastering reading, because in common with most 'world class' skills, a skilled reader will probably have spent a thousand hours reading.

Consequently, teachers really should not beat themselves up for failing to help a dyslexic child learn to read fluently. There's some intrinsic problem with the LEARNING process(es) involved.

3.4 Phase 2: Cerebellar Deficit Theory

Nicolson and Fawcett Theory
Phase 2 (1995-2001)
The Cerebellar Deficit Theory

We had actually completed this work by the mid 1990s, and realized that to further investigate the learning processes we needed to look at the underlying neuroscience. The 90s were the decade of the brain, and more was discovered about the brain in that decade than the total previous progress.

From my perspective the major change was the transformation of the role of the cerebellum from motor skill coordinator to 'all skills coordinator and learner', and in particular the emerging evidence that the cerebellum was centrally involved in language fluency. This formed the basis for our cerebellar deficit framework.

3.4.1 Theory: The Cerebellum

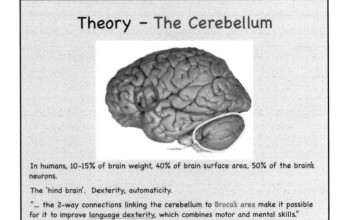

Theory – The Cerebellum

In humans, 10-15% of brain weight, 40% of brain surface area, 50% of the brain's neurons.

The 'hind brain'. Dexterity, automaticity.

"... the 2-way connections linking the cerebellum to Broca's area make it possible for it to improve language dexterity, which combines motor and mental skills."

The cerebellum is shown above ringed in yellow. It has long been known to be centrally involved in fluency of skill execution. It is a huge organ, connected to almost all brain regions (and the rest of the body), and contains more than half the brain's neurons. Unlike the neocortex it does its job efficiently, reliably, without fuss, and without our knowing anything about it at all!

It is only with the advent of brain imaging that its ubiquitous role in all sorts of processing - from taste to speech to reading to automaticity - has been revealed.

The first claim of cerebellar involvement in cognition was made in 1989 by Leiner, Leiner and Dow, and that is the source of this quotation - Broca's area is shown in red - about language dexterity.

"... the 2-way connections linking the cerebellum to Broca's area make it possible for it to improve language dexterity, which combines motor and mental skills" [46].

Their hypothesis - in terms both of connectivity and function - has been completely vindicated (in normally achieving individuals) by subsequent cognitive neuroscience research.

3.4.2 Cerebellar Activation in Cognitive Tasks

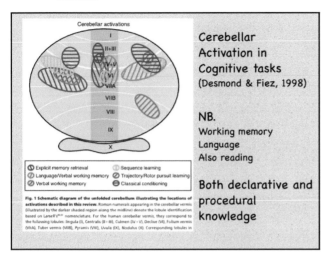

Cerebellar Activation in Cognitive tasks (Desmond & Fiez, 1998)

NB.
Working memory
Language
Also reading

Both declarative and procedural knowledge

This figure summarizes the established role of the cerebellum in cognitive activities. The cerebellum is shown flattened out. The vermis is shown as the darker stripe in the middle. There is contralateral connection of cerebellar cortex to neocortex, so the right lateral cerebellum is connected to the left cerebral cortex - the language areas - and to the right hand side of your body [47].

Note the multiple skills involving cerebellar activation. We have classical conditioning, we have pursuit learning, but also we have the cognition ones - explicit memory retrieval, language / verbal working memory, verbal working memory, and sequence learning, as shown in those regions.

Note also the distributed nature of the activation, with different regions involved in different tasks, but with also overlapping distributions of some skills.

It is particularly important for our dyslexia framework to note the link to the working memory, language and reading circuits together with both declarative and procedural knowledge.

3.4.3 Dyslexia: An ontogenetic Causal Chain

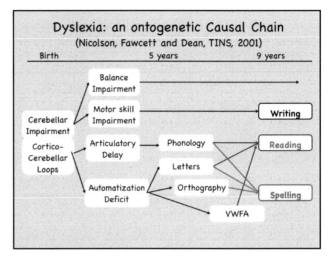

In a range of innovative studies we established clear, direct and indirect evidence of cerebellar deficits associated with dyslexia - functional imaging, prism adaptation, eye blink conditioning, cerebellar signs.

This led to a major achievement in a 2001 paper in Trends in Neuroscience - the creation of a developmental model of how the reading, writing and spelling deficits arise. Ontogenetic means developmental [38].

This is what we came up with. Note that it moves from birth through 5 years to 9 years from left to right. We start off with a cerebellar impairment - possibly attributable to abnormal brain neural migration processes - from birth (or pre-birth). We also note that it is possible that the other parts of the brain - the cortico-cerebellar loops - are involved.

What effects would this have? Cerebellar impairment is very likely to lead to balance impairment and also to motor skill impairment, articulatory delay (articulation is a motor skill) and also automatization deficit.

What implications would this have over the years?

- Balance impairment - probably would not get into the school teams for sport, but not directly related to literacy.
- Motor skill impairment - similar but in this case it has a direct effect upon handwriting skill.
- Articulatory delay is an interesting one, because it is now known that expressive speech and receptive speech - phonology - are directly linked, and so

articulatory delay would be hypothesized to lead to phonological differences.

- And automatization deficit would lead to problems with identifying the individual letters, the spellings and, indeed, later on the development of the neural circuits for the Visual Word Form Area.

What effects would these have on reading? The phonology, the letters and the Visual Word Form Area would directly impact on the development of the reading circuitry. And the phonology, the letters and the orthography would directly impact upon the spelling performance.

So this combination of impairments will lead to significant difficulties in learning to read - you see we have a 'triple whammy' here, both for reading and for spelling, but actually a different set of problems. This is consistent with the findings of different genetic underpinnings to phonological and orthographic (that is, the spelling) problems.

Angela and I are particularly proud of this chart. It provides a principled explanation of the three criterial difficulties for dyslexic children (reading, writing and spelling). And it explains why there are phonological deficits and orthographic deficits. And it explains why there are various secondary symptoms not related to literacy. It provides a principled method for screening for dyslexia BEFORE a child fails to learn to rea.

For the first time in any discipline, it provided a link between development, the brain and school achievement, explaining our highest level cognitive skills of literacy in terms of the underlying developmental processes. Birth, brain and behavior blueprint in one chart!

3.5 Research Phase 3: Procedural Learning Deficit

Nicolson and Fawcett Theory
Phase 3 (2001-2007)
Procedural Learning Deficit

A further topic which has emerged more recently is the proof that many brain regions are involved in the acquisition and the execution of cognitive and motor skills, and that therefore it is important to consider the system as a whole, not just parts of it.

This neural systems approach forms the basis for our integrative recent procedural learning difficulties framework.

For the first time, neuroscience developed a classification of four different fundamental learning processes, with three of them occurring automatically, a legacy of the many million years old vertebrate machinery, and one of them much more recent, more dependent on thought.

For ease of remembering, I am calling them brain-based learning and mind-based learning respectively (which is short-hand for some complex concepts!)

As with everything else in the brain, these learning systems combine (or sometimes compete).

3.5.1 Learning Mechanisms and the Brain

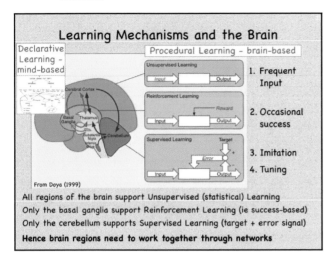

The three learning types shown on the right of the figure are the 'primitive' types that we have inherited from the first vertebrates - fish, crocodiles, lizards. They are generically called procedural learning. I am calling them 'brain-based learning' [48].

The unsupervised learning, also known as statistical learning, occurs automatically by just frequent occurrence. The brain creates self-organizing networks that automatically learn to classify say the speech sounds in each child's native tongue.

The reinforcement learning is where one is given a reward for doing something - some food or a smartie, whatever. Occasional success. It is very important to be able to work out what caused that. We have specialized machinery, running via the basal ganglia, which help us to work that out.

And then supervised learning is actually error-dependent learning where we know what we are trying to achieve and we get an error signal to indicate how close our action was to achieving its target, and therefore we can try to improve our performance over time. For example, trying to trace out a shape. There are two major forms, imitation when we are trying to get started and then tuning as we get more skilled.

All regions of the brain support unsupervised, statistical learning. Only the basal ganglia support reinforcement-based learning, the success-based learning. And only the cerebellum supports supervised learning, where there is a target and an error signal. And hence the brain regions need to work together through networks. If you want to do

supervised learning, then you have to get the cerebellum as part of your team, along with the other parts of the brain involved.

Those three types of learning are generically called procedural learning, and I am going to refer to them as brain-based learning. They are primitive (but powerful) forms of learning that go back to the crocodile!

The other form of learning, which is much more specific to humans, is Declarative Learning, which I am calling mind-based learning. And that is actually one of the ways that we use our knowledge of the world to improve our memory and performance.

I go through those in the next figure.

3.5.2 Declarative vs Procedural Language Systems

> **Declarative vs Procedural Memory / Language systems**
>
> 1. Declarative Memory System – 'Mind-based'
>   - The mental encyclopaedia
>   - temporal-lobe, hippocampus
>   - storage and use of knowledge of facts and events.
>   - 'ventral route'
>   - Conscious access
> 2. Procedural Memory System – 'Brain-based'
>   - The mental grammar, rule-governed
>   - network of specific frontal, basal-ganglia, parietal and cerebellar structures
>   - underlies procedural memory, which supports the learning and execution of habit-based language skills, especially those involving sequences.
>   - 'dorsal route'
>   - No conscious access

I had been a bit confused about how this distinction between procedural learning and declarative learning could work, because I had assumed that declarative learning was directly related to language and thought, of which we're consciously aware, but not to motor skills, which are procedural.

I realized, however, that this was plain wrong when I read a paper by Michael Ullman which claimed that in fact there are two language systems - declarative memory and procedural memory [49].

This integrated a whole range of findings in the literature, and made sense to me of the fact that there are different types of language skill, some of them explicit, available to conscious introspection, and some procedural and not consciously penetrable.

These are the characteristics of the Declarative Memory System - the 'mind-based' one. It is the mental encyclopedia. The circuits involve the temporal lobe and the hippocampus, and it is valuable for storage and use of knowledge of facts and events. The circuits are known as the 'ventral route' anatomically, and, a key point, we have conscious access to our declarative processing, which is why I call it 'mind-based'.

By contrast, the Procedural Memory System is 'brain-based'. It does the mental grammar, the rules of grammar, and involves a network of specific frontal, basal-ganglia, parietal and cerebellar structures. It underlies procedural memory, which supports the learning and execution of habit-based language skills, especially those involving sequences. Anatomically it is known as the 'dorsal route'. And we have no conscious access.

For example, we just 'know' how to string our words together into a coherent sentence, one at a time, and it 'trips off the tongue' just like that. But we have no conscious access to the process (which remains a complete mystery to me!) - that is the procedural language system. And we can say whether a statement is grammatically correct or not without knowing why - that is our implicit rule-based procedural language skill.

One can often carry out a skill in either way, and Ullman makes the interesting claim that these systems compete to do the task, with the first system to be ready actually doing it.

This framework led directly to our third framework for dyslexia, which is the Procedural Learning Deficit hypothesis. Following Ullman, we speculated that most developmental disorders might be attributable to problems in some form of the Procedural Memory system.

Many developmental disorders are attributable to abnormal function of the Procedural Memory (brain-based) system - I am calling it the Procedural Learning system, to highlight its role in plasticity as well as memory

And there are two different Procedural Learning systems, the motor Procedural Learning system and the language Procedural Learning system.

For dyslexia, I argue that we have Specific Procedural Learning Difficulty - specific to the language-cerebellum, but involving other Procedural Learning components to a greater or lesser degree.

This is in fact a refinement of the classic four levels analysis from behavior - cognition - brain - genetics. You may remember that our automatization deficit hypothesis was at the cognitive level, and our cerebellar deficit hypothesis was at the brain level - both explaining the same general findings.

And our procedural learning deficit hypothesis is at what we have called the neural systems level, in between the brain and cognition. And we believe that this neural systems level of explanation is a particularly fruitful one at which one can explain a whole range of different developmental disorders, as I show below.

3.5.3 The Procedural Learning Deficit (PLD) Hypothesis

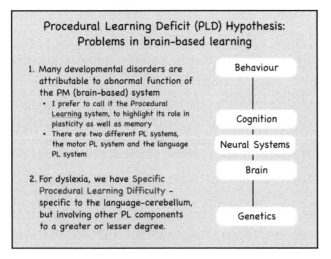

3.5.4 Declarative and Procedural Circuits in Developmental Disorders

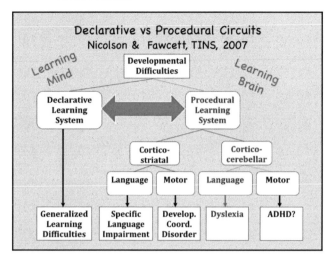

This is an article taken again from Trends in Neuroscience, a 2007 paper. Developmental difficulties can be differentiated into the Declarative Learning system and the Procedural Learning system [35].

Taking the Declarative circuit, if there is a problem in declarative learning, this will lead to generalized learning problems, and hence poor reading but with no discrepancy, because there will be poor performance across the board intellectually. So, for us, we would call those generalized learning difficulties.

The procedural learning circuits - which I have called the Learning Brain in the figure - can be divided into cortico-striatal circuit and the cortico-cerebellar circuit. Striatal means basal ganglia. We can divide the cortico-striatal system into language and motor.

Following Ullman's approach we allocate Specific Language Impairment to abnormal function in the language aspects of the cortico-striatal system. Developmental Coordination Disorder (clumsiness) to the motor component of that system. If we turn now to the cortico-cerebellar system, again we can distinguish between language and motor. The motor is probably attention deficit disorder, whereas the language component - the Specific Procedural Learning Difficulty - is dyslexia.

Now, here I highlight the fact that we are moving toward strengths at last - because the procedural system and the declarative system cooperate or compete. Consequently, if you are not using your procedural system as much, then you will be able to use your declarative system more, and so you may gain declarative strengths which allow you to compensate for any procedural difficulties.

3.5.5 Recent evidence for the SPLD framework

Recent Evidence for the SPLD Framework

- An early study in Oxford (Stoodley at al., 2006) established problems in implicit motor learning for dyslexic adults.
- A meta-analysis of serial reaction time studies (implicit learning) shows a consistent deficit, coupled with consistent problems in procedural learning (Lum, Ullman and Conti Ramsden, 2013)
- Deficit in consolidation of procedural skill automatization in dyslexia in children. Also greater impact on procedural learning of letters than motor sequences (Gabay, Shiff and Vakil, 2012)
- Children with dyslexia have better learning and retention in declarative memory than typically developing children (Hedenius & Ullman, 2013).

There is now extensive evidence for the Specific Procedural Learning Difficulties framework.

An early study by Catherine Stoodley, Edward Harrison and John Stein in Oxford revealed problems in implicit motor learning for dyslexic adults [44].

And in fact a recent meta-analysis of studies of serial reaction time, that is implicit learning - which is procedural memory - show a consistent deficit for dyslexia [45].

And we have recently identified a deficit in consolidation of procedural skill automatization in dyslexic children [46]. Furthermore, a recent study by Yafit Gabay and her colleagues revealed a greater difficulty in procedural learning for letters than for motor sequences, thereby implicating the language component of the procedural learning circuits [47].

Of particular interest, however, Michael Ullman and Martina Hedenius showed that children with dyslexia have better learning and retention of declarative memory than typically developing children. This is an important finding because it is one of the few studies to have found significantly better performance for dyslexics than age-matched controls - a strength for declarative learning! [43].

3.5.6 Explanatory Power of the SPLD framework

> ## Explanatory Power
>
> 1. Provides a principled explanation of the various disorders in terms of established neural networks
> 2. Highlights the interplay between the different disorders
> 3. Consistent with extensive evidence of difficulties in procedural learning, implicit learning and statistical learning
> 4. But it stops at 8 years old
> 5. And it doesn't explain the pattern of strengths

There is therefore solid evidence for the framework, and again it has been welcomed by researchers in the other developmental disorders.

But how is it doing in terms of explanatory power? You may remember I criticized the phonological deficit hypothesis for lack of explanatory power.

SPLD does provide a principled explanation of the various disorders in terms of established neural networks. It highlights the interplay between the different disorders. It is consistent with extensive evidence of difficulties in procedural learning, implicit learning and statistical learning in dyslexia.

But it stops at 8 years old. And it does not explain the pattern of strengths.

So for Positive Dyslexia it is not sufficient.

3.6 Why Strengths: Delayed Neural Commitment

> ## Why Strengths?
> ## Delayed Neural Commitment

This was the stimulus for the fourth component of our analyses, which I have called Delayed Neural Commitment.

I put our work on the underlying learning processes together with concepts derived from developmental cognitive neuroscience, inspired by the theoretical understanding of how infants develop language and speech, following the work of Pat Kuhl and her colleagues, and the neuro-constructivist approach initiated by Annette Karmiloff-Smith and Mark Johnson [50-52].

3.6.1 Strength theories of dyslexia

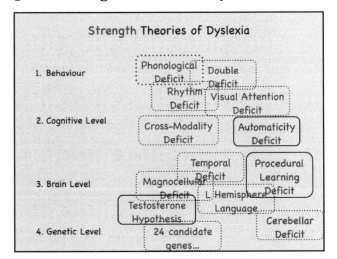

Let us consider the theories of dyslexia (Figure 3.1.5) from a strengths perspective. We have a really wide range of potential explanations of dyslexia, but few of these give an explanation of strengths, as we shall see. Phonological deficit gives no explanation of strengths, and so I have represented it with a dotted outline. Double deficit, rhythm deficit, cross-modality, visual deficit, left hemisphere, temporal deficit, candidate genes - these are all looking at deficits. Magnocellular deficit, and even the cerebellar deficit - they are all phrased in terms of deficits, and have no explanation for the potential strengths [29, 31, 36, 53-55].

The testosterone hypothesis is an interesting one, suggesting that the problems arise from neural migration. It is not right in detail but might be right in principle. It is consistent with procedural and automatization and cerebellar deficits, amongst others [56].

3.6.2 Automaticity

Automaticity

- Effects of automatization
  - Neural commitment – small, dedicated cell assembly
  - Encapsulation
  - Loss of conscious access
  - Stimulus-response 'habit'
- Up-side
  - Fast
  - Efficient
  - Takes no conscious capacity

Let us therefore look again at automaticity. The effects of automatization are neural commitment - which creates small, dedicated cell assemblies; encapsulation, so that the assembly works by itself without needing to communicate with the rest of the brain; loss of conscious access, and basically a stimulus-response 'habit'.

The up-side of this is that it is fast, efficient, and takes up no conscious capacity.

If you think about a skill like driving - which is one we acquire relatively late - the key aspects are that we set up specialized neural circuits to change gear, to monitor the road, and to undertake all the sub-skills without needing to concentrate on them. And a skilled driver can actually drive and talk perfectly happily.

That is the big advantage of automaticity - that it is fast, effortless and efficient. And almost all the time this is just great.

3.6.3 Automaticity - does it have a down-side?

Automaticity – does it have a down-side?

1. Unlearning
   - It takes a lot longer to 'unlearn' a habit than to learn it in the first place
2. Loss of declarative access
   - Once automatised, no longer available for conscious access
   - Can't integrate that information with other declarative information
3. Over-writing of previous skills
   - New skills replace old skills
   - May lose the non-language skills that characterise young children
     - Exceptional nonverbal memory
     - Exceptional spatial skills!?
4. Loss of mental flexibility
   - Between stimulus and response there is a space. In that space is our power to choose our response. In our response lies our growth and our freedom (Viktor Frankl).

But does automaticity have a down-side?

Do you have any bad habits!? Once one has a bad habit it is harder to 'unlearn' it than to learn a good habit in the first place This is also pretty clear in the case of building up complex skills. If you just practice one aspect in isolation - whether it is the tennis forehand, or phonological analysis - if you do it in isolation you will not build it into the complete skill later on.

There is of course a loss of declarative access. Once automatized, it is no longer available for conscious access. The down-side of that - and it is a serious down-side - is that it is self-contained and therefore cannot be integrated with other declarative information.

Skill automatization also has the problem that it over-writes previous skills because the new skills replace the old skills. You may, for instance, lose the non-language skills that characterize young children, who may have an exceptional nonverbal memory and exceptional spatial skills. That is, you will lose knowledge interconnectedness, as Brock Eide would say [23].

3.6.4 Declarative Specialization - the Up-side

> ### Declarative Specialization – the upside?
>
> - Declarative and procedural processing tend to work both together and in opposition (Ullman). Generally work on a winner-takes-all basis so that the first system to compute the answer gets strengthened
> - If procedural processing is slower, the declarative processing will continue to 'win' and therefore the tendency to keep using it will continue
> - Hence skills involving a strong declarative component will be distinctive strengths
> - Skills involving 'knowledge expertise' rather than 'skill expertise'
> - In fact, the majority of 21st century skills!

At last we are talking about strengths! Declarative specialization - the up-side.

The declarative specialization biases the brain's processing in that particular direction, it avoids all the downsides of automaticity, it allows storage of very detailed knowledge - what Brock calls the Narrative strengths.

Declarative and procedural processing tend to work both together and in opposition, as Michael Ullman has shown. This generally works on a winner-takes-all basis so that the first system to compute the answer gets strengthened [57].

If procedural processing is slower, the declarative processing will continue to 'win' and therefore the tendency to keep using it will continue. Hence skills involving a strong declarative component will be distinctive strengths.

That is, skills involving 'knowledge expertise' rather than 'skill expertise'.

And, in fact, the majority of 21st century skills, as I demonstrate in Chapter 7!

3.6.5 The Delayed Neural Commitment Hypothesis

> ### The Delayed Neural Commitment Hypothesis
>
> 1. Dyslexic individuals are relatively slow to automatise skills
> 2. They therefore show 'delayed neural commitment'
> 3. This occurs in most skills, especially language-based ones
> 4. While generally DNC is associated with slower and more effortful processing, it can endow advantages, especially in circumstances where it is useful to maintain earlier skills, or valuable to combine two different skills which do not normally occur within the same 'time window'
> 5. DNC can therefore lead to two crucial advantages:
>   - Retention of access to pre-linguistic skills
>   - Combination of knowledge from two different domains

So that finally brings us to the Delayed Neural Commitment hypothesis. This postulates that dyslexic individuals are relatively slow to automatize skills. They therefore show 'delayed neural commitment'. This occurs in most skills, especially language-based ones. This leads to slower processing, and more effortful processing, and difficulties with multi-tasking.

Delayed neural commitment in general means that habits are less strong, and the mind is used to supervising with conscious attention even relatively simple actions. Consequently neural commitment takes longer and might not ever occur.

While generally DNC is associated with slower and more effortful processing, it can endow advantages, especially in circumstances where it is useful to maintain earlier skills, or valuable to combine two different skills which don't normally occur within the same 'time window'.

Delayed Neural Commitment, therefore, can lead to two crucial advantages:

- retention of access to pre-linguistic skills; and
- combination of knowledge from two different domains.

And these benefits can continue to keep building through adult life.

3.6.6 Evidence for the Delayed Neural Commitment Hypothesis

> **Evidence for the DNC Hypothesis**
>
> - Neural commitment is the primary mechanism for language specialization in infants [Kuhl, 2004]. See Chapter 5.
> - Reading delay, especially the transition from logographic to alphabetic, and then the transition from alphabetic to orthographic (VWFA may never develop fully)
> - Automatization deficit etc. [Nicolson and Fawcett studies]. Statistical, procedural, implicit learning weaknesses (Hedenius et al, 2013; Menghini et al., 2010; Vicari et al., 2005)
> - No sensitivity to speech sounds at birth (hence no learning in womb) [Lyytinen et al., 2010; Molfese, 2000]
> - For some children, primitive reflexes not unlearned [McPhillips et al, 2000]
> - Delay in speech milestones and in some cases motor milestones [Lyytinen et al., 2004; Viholainen et al., 2002]

Neural commitment is the primary mechanism for language specialization in infants - Pat Kuhl's work, which I will describe in Chapter 5.

Reading delay, especially the transition from logographic to alphabetic, and then the transition from alphabetic to orthographic, does seem to be particularly problematic for dyslexic children. The Visual Word Form Area may never develop fully.

Our work on the automatization deficit and related theories provided initial evidence. More recently, several researchers have revealed deficits in statistical, procedural, and implicit learning weaknesses [57].

Interesting evidence also derives from infant studies:

- Studies have revealed no sensitivity to speech sounds at birth, and hence no learning in the womb [58].
- Furthermore, Martin McPhillips has shown that for some children, the primitive reflexes do not get unlearned [59].
- And again, further work suggests that there is delay in speech milestones and in some cases motor milestones, in the influential (Jyvyskala) Finnish studies on the development of dyslexia from pre-birth to 10 years old run by Heikki Lyytinen and his colleagues [60].

3.6.7 Ontogeny to Adulthood

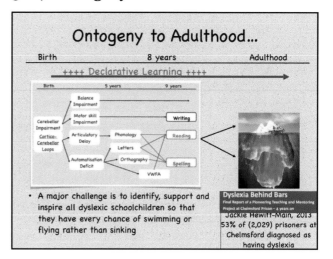

- A major challenge is to identify, support and inspire all dyslexic schoolchildren so that they have every chance of swimming or flying rather than sinking

We are now, finally, in position to add to that chart that I provided for the cerebellar deficit hypothesis. Our original hypothesis for the cerebellar deficit hypothesis is shown in the box.

This time the timescale goes up to adulthood. Note the Declarative Learning strengths continuing all the way through.

This framework highlights the 'fork in the road' for dyslexia. Some children will 'fly' - they cope with the problems at school and go on to live to their strengths. Others - the majority unfortunately, as indicated by the iceberg analogy - will 'sink', as indicated by this study by Jackie Hewitt-Main which established that over half the prisoners in Chelmsford jail in the UK are dyslexic [61].

Therefore, the major challenge for us is to identify, support and inspire all dyslexic schoolchildren so that they have every chance of swimming or flying rather than sinking.

3.7 Delayed Neural Commitment and the established strengths of dyslexia

How well does DNC explain the
established strengths?

There are solid theoretical reasons for the Delayed Neural Commitment, but of course the real test in terms of Positive Dyslexia is - how well is it able to handle the strengths of dyslexia, and especially the empirical findings we reported in Chapter 2?

3.7.1 Sources of Potential Advantage under Delayed Neural Commitment

Sources of Potential Advantage under DNC

- Declarative specialization
- Less 'pruning' of primitive capabilities
- Extended sensitive periods allow longer learning period into late adolescence and adulthood
- Reduced commitment / compartmentalization allows greater cognitive processing and flexibility
- More cross-talk between different brain regions and senses etc. allows more integrative processing.

It is evident that in some situations, 'look before you leap' and 'more haste less speed' make eminent sense! We will see in Chapter 5 that infants born in a bilingual environment take longer to 'neurally commit' to the more complex linguistic ienvironment in which they are immersed, but once they have

developed the necessary more sophisicated processing architecture this endows advantages from executive function to less likelihood of Alzheimers!

Here I list sources of potential advantage under DNC.

- Declarative specialization
- less 'pruning' of primitive capabilities
- extended sensitive periods which allow a longer learning period into late adolescence and adulthood
- reduced commitment and compartmentalization - which allows greater cognitive processing and flexibility
- and more cross-talk between the brain regions and the senses which allows more integrative processing.

3.7.2 MIND Strengths and Delayed Neural Commitment

'MIND strengths' and
Delayed Neural Commitment!?

Material Reasoning
- Ability to follow non-verbal actions - retention of primitive skills
- Visualisation abilities - retention and integration of visual skills

Interconnected Reasoning
- Integration of different perspectives - less compartmentalisation
- Big picture thinking - higher level, non-sequential thinking?

Narrative Reasoning
- Personal narrative - access to primitive experiential knowledge
- 'Telling the story' - combined big picture and communication

Dynamic Reasoning
- Intuitive reasoning - expertise plus global thinking
- Vision - big picture thinking

We can consider how well the theoretical framework compares with the MIND strengths empirically derived by Brock and Fernette Eide:

Material Reasoning

- The ability to follow non-verbal actions - retention of primitive skills;
- Visualization ability - retention and integration of visual skills.

Interconnected Reasoning

- Integration of different perspectives - less compartmentalization;

- Big picture thinking - higher level, non-sequential thinking?

Narrative Reasoning

- Personal narrative - access to primitive experiential knowledge;
- 'Telling the story' - combined big picture and communication.

Dynamic Reasoning

- Intuitive reasoning - expertise plus global thinking;
- Vision - big picture thinking.

I think therefore that Delayed Neural Commitment gives a very good account of the key aspects of the MIND strengths.

3.7.3 Strengths Decathlon and Delayed Neural Commitment

'Strengths Decathlon' and
Delayed Neural Commitment!?

1. The Cognitive Skills Triad
   - Visuo-Spatial Skills – access to more primitive skills
   - Big Picture– non-sequential thinking
   - Creativity– non-habitual, interconnected thinking
2. The Social Skills Triad
   - Empathy– more understanding of individual differences
   - Teamwork – long-standing coping strategy!
   - Communication– more experience, big picture
3. The Work Skills Triad
   - Determination / Resilience– university of life!
   - Proactivity– need to think and plan ahead
   - Flexible Coping – not habit-bound, used to difficulties
4. Unconventional thinking – extended learning and integration period

How about our own Strengths Decathlon and Delayed Neural Commitment?

The Cognitive Skills Triad:

- Visuo-Spatial Skills - access to more primitive skills;
- Big Picture- non-sequential thinking;
- Creativity- non-habitual, interconnected thinking.

The Social Skills Triad:

- Empathy- more understanding of individual differences;
- Teamwork - long-standing coping strategy!
- Communication - more experience, big picture.

The Work Skills Triad:

- Determination / Resilience - university of life!
- Proactivity - need to think and plan ahead;
- Flexible Coping - not habit-bound, used to having difficulties.

Unconventional thinking - arises from the extended learning and integration period

So, I think that the DNC again gives a very good account of the key aspects of the Dyslexia Decathlon.

3.7.4 Conventional and Unconventional Thinking Processes

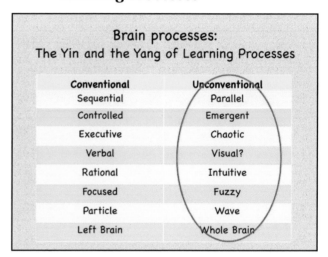

The reintroduction of unconventional thinking reminds me of unfinished business. When I introduced this term in Chapter 2, I rather ducked the issue of defining it properly, but we are now in position to have a go, on the basis of the Delayed Neural Commitment hypothesis.

Consider these distinctions for Conventional versus Unconventional Thinking:

Sequential vs Parallel; Controlled vs Emergent; Executive vs Chaotic; Verbal vs Visual; Rational vs Intuitive; Focused vs Fuzzy; Particle vs Wave; Left brain vs Whole brain.

Those are the classic definitions of conventional versus unconventional skills. But which side corresponds to dyslexia under Delayed Neural Commitment!?

I have characterized dyslexic learning as a relative weakness for brain-based learning and a relative strength for mind-based learning. At first sight, surely this means that the mind-based processing must have a more controlled, attentional component. The verbal, rational left hand column.

In fact, it is the other way round. The conventional brain-based processes derive from taking a complex network and making it simpler, so that processing becomes an encapsulated, habit-based, series of sequential events (actions), that is they're sequential. They are the left hand column!

The dyslexic mind does not make such efficient and isolated units, and so it maintains connectivity with the rest of the mind. So the dyslexic thinking is much more global, intuitive, chaotic, more like a wave than a particle.

And so the dyslexic brain is indeed the right hand, unconventional, column.

3.8 Why are there reading problems under Delayed Neural Commitment?

Why are there reading problems under DNC?

I will now address the question of why there are reading problems under Delayed Neural Commitment. I have already provided our 'ontogenetic causal chain' explanation, which builds on weaknesses in the neural circuits involving the cerebellum and other brain regions to provide explanations of the reading, writing and spelling problems.

But, in addition, DNC provides an explanation in terms of neural circuit development, as I explain next.

3.8.1 Normal Reading Acquisition

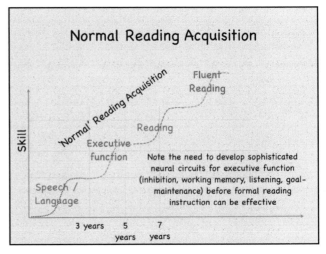

This figure tries to represent the extraordinary 'brain construction' processes that are needed before a child can read fluently. First, of course, he or she must acquire and automatize speech and language, then 'executive functions', then reading, and then moving on to fluent reading. This 'mind construction' process goes on in tandem with the learning-to-read process, and for normally achieving children, the teaching process is well timed to allow synergy between the explicit schooling and the implicit circuit-building.

Consequently, the executive function circuits are developed for working memory, attention, listening, goal-maintenance and resilience. So by the age of 9 or 10 all the structures, skills and knowledge for fluent reading are in place, as illustrated by the Yeatman picture of the 10 year old I showed earlier.

3.8.2 Delayed Neural Commitment: Sink or Fly

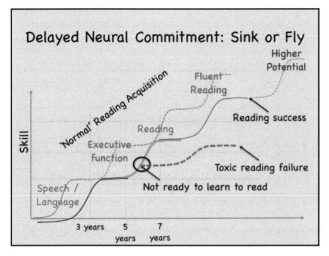

Now, what about dyslexia? This is the situation for dyslexia, using Delayed Neural Commitment.

Speech and language develop a bit slower, but that in itself is not a problem, there is no real hurry. The executive function neural circuitry is also built more slowly, perhaps becoming mature at 7 years rather than 6.

If the reading process is able to proceed, reading is acquired slowly, but securely, perhaps by the age of 11, and this then can indeed lead to better-than-normal performance.

Unfortunately, formal teaching methods are often introduced too early, relying on fragile executive processes that are not fully mature, so that the child is not ready to learn to read.

This can lead to catastrophic breakdown of the process, and what I have called toxic reading failure, as I explain in chapter 4.

3.9 Conclusions on 'Why Dyslexia'

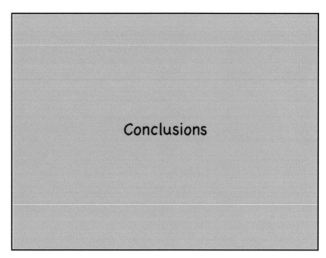

It is time to finish the chapter!

3.9.1 Chapter Conclusions

> ## Conclusions
>
> 1. Most 'causal' theories of dyslexia are silent on why there might be strengths
> 2. Extensive research has demonstrated that dyslexic children learn badly for procedural 'brain-based' tasks but learn well for declarative 'mind-based' tasks. We propose that 'Delayed Neural Commitment' provides a principled explanation integrating a range of previously disparate findings
> 3. Excitingly, DNC also appears to handle the empirical data on strengths - the MIND strengths and the decathlon - that have been established in non-theoretical work
> 4. It therefore provides a unifying framework of considerable significance both for Deficit Dyslexia and Positive Dyslexia

My conclusions are again very positive.

Most 'causal' theories of dyslexia are silent on why there might be strengths.

The Delayed Neural Commitment hypothesis integrates my three causal theories for the causes of dyslexia - automaticity deficit, cerebellar deficit and procedural deficit. These theories in turn subsume major theories including the Phonological Deficit.

Extensive research has demonstrated that dyslexic children learn badly for procedural 'brain-based' tasks but learn well for declarative 'mind-based' tasks.

'Delayed Neural Commitment' provides a principled explanation integrating a range of previously disparate findings.

Excitingly, DNC also appears to handle the empirical data on strengths - the MIND strengths and the Dyslexia Decathlon - that have been established in non-theoretical work.

It therefore provides a unifying framework of considerable significance both for Deficit Dyslexia and for Positive Dyslexia.

3.9.2 End of Chapter 3

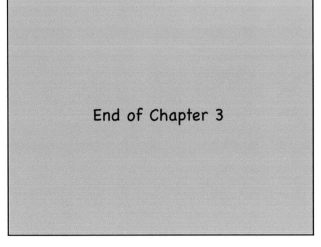

This has been a theoretical chapter, presenting and integrating a range of explanations of dyslexia. The results were exciting, with the need to explain strengths giving a fruitful lead for theory development, strongly supporting the goals of Positive Dyslexia and providing a theoretical explanation for the strengths we described previously.

Chapter 4 follows this up by considering the implications of the Delayed Neural Commitment framework for early reading support. And the results can be grim if too little time is available for maturation.

Chapter 4: Failing to Learn and Learning to Fail

4.1 Chapter Introduction

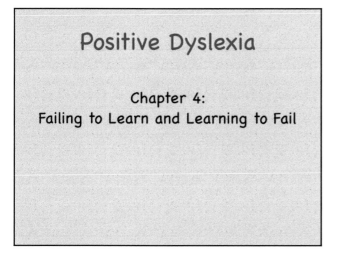

In Chapter 1 I presented the logic behind Positive Dyslexia, the need to work to strengths rather than weaknesses. In Chapters 2 and 3 I considered the strengths of dyslexia - what they are and why they are, ending up with the concept of delayed neural commitment.

I also highlighted the fact that for dyslexia it seems to be 'fly or drown', and in this chapter I am looking at the down side - why dyslexic children often fail to thrive.

4.1.1 The Positive Dyslexia Journey

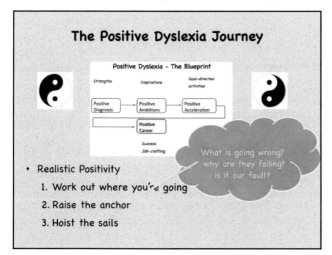

Here is the Positive Dyslexia Journey. The first stage is to have a Positive Assessment, based on strengths

as well as weaknesses. In Chapters 2 and 3 I have established what the strengths are and why they arise. Next we need to allow each individual to identify their own strengths and to start developing them.

But there is a problem, life is not just about strengths - the other side of the coin from the positive psychology. I think I can get it across best by this analogy of going on a sea journey - which I have called realistic positivity.

For a successful voyage you have to work out where you are heading, you have to raise the anchor, you have to hoist the sails. We have worked out where are heading. Positive Psychology is good for hoisting the sails. But we need first to raise the anchor - to find what the barriers are to progress. Indeed, I have missed out a stage - first we need to build the boat!

So in this chapter I go through the initial problems in getting started.

What is it that goes wrong? Why are these children failing? Is it our fault?

4.1.2 Green field, brown field and toxic learning

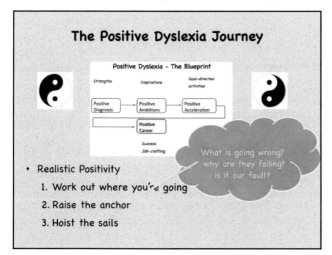

I will continue with another anecdote. It relates to my days playing tennis. I was a reasonable, club-standard, tennis player. I had a good all-round game, but I had a weakness with my backhand volley.

I went to see the junior pro. The junior pro could see that I wasn't doing it well but couldn't tell me how to do it better. He said "I'm just going to have to teach you from scratch, the way I'd teach anyone."

So I went to the senior pro. The senior pro looked carefully. He was able to see what I was doing wrong and tell me how to adapt my action so that I could do it right. And after that in fact my backhand volley became my best shot.

The point is that it is much easier to start from scratch than to correct a bad habit. It takes much more expertise to overcome a bad habit.

This brings me on to the analogy of green field versus brown field learning. You will be familiar with the idea of a building on a green field site - there is nothing there but grass, so you just need to lay on the utilities, and everything is simple. It is building from scratch. As opposed to the brown field site, where there has already been building, there may be old buildings, old foundations, even some toxic earth if it was an industrial site. This is much more difficult.

It is even worse with learning - bad learning experiences cause 'toxic patches' in the brain, so that if the situation triggers them, you go into an extremely non-positive state.

Consider your nightmare activities - what would you do anything to avoid!?

For me it's singing and dancing. A karaoke evening is my idea of purgatory. And this is the residue of being ridiculed for my useless singing and dancing all through childhood. We all have these 'stinking fish' activities - activities that we try to avoid at all costs and feel really embarrassed about. Unfortunately, for dyslexic children that stinking fish is the core school activity of reading.

4.1.3 Plan of Chapter 4

> **Plan of Section**
>
> - Why do Dyslexic Children Fail?
> - Math Anxiety
> - Learning Failure
>   - Learned Helplessness
>   - Mental scratches and mental abscesses
>   - Disabling Learning
> - Conclusions

That provides the rationale for this chapter. I am going through why it is that most dyslexic children fail. The core idea here is that of learned helplessness, where after a series of bad experiences, you just cannot seem to get a mental grip on that topic or activity.

I motivate the discussion with the well known problems of mathematics anxiety, which causes this sort of behavior in many highly intelligent people, and I then go on to develop the idea that each experience of failure leads to what I call a 'mental scratch'.

If these mental scratches are not allowed to heal by success or time, that is after a series of adverse, ongoing and inescapable failures, a 'mental abscess' is caused that is almost impossible to heal, and this essentially prevents any learning in that situation.

That is, the experiences have actually caused a learning disability - as for me and karaoke, and for many of us and mathematics. But for dyslexia it's reading that seems to cause those problems.

4.1.4 The Positive Dyslexia Paradox

> ## The Positive Dyslexia Paradox
>
> - I argued earlier that dyslexia is associated with a range of strengths, including teamwork and empathy
> - And yet, this is only for a minority of dyslexic adults.
> - For the majority of dyslexic adults, dyslexia is associated with failure, and there is a disproportionate number of dyslexic adults in prison
> - How can this be!?
> - It's not enough just to set the intended destination for our Positive Dyslexia voyage, and to hoist the sails, first we need to pull up the anchor, the things that hold us back...

This raises the issue of 'the Positive Dyslexia Paradox'. I argued earlier that dyslexia is associated with a range of strengths, including teamwork and empathy. And yet, this is only for a minority of dyslexic adults. For the majority of dyslexic adults, dyslexia is associated with failure, and there is a disproportionate number of dyslexic adults in prison. How can this be, given these strengths!?

It is not enough just to set the intended destination for our Positive Dyslexia voyage, and to hoist the sails.

First we need to pull up the anchor, the things that hold us back...

4.1.5 Dyslexia Behind Bars

> ## Dyslexia Behind Bars
> **Final Report of a Pioneering Teaching and Mentoring Project at Chelmsford Prison – 4 years on**
>
> - INTERVIEWS with all 2,029 prisoners at Chelmsford Prison discovered that:
>   - Before this project started, 60% of incoming prisoners opted to do neither work nor training for fear of revealing their illiteracy.
>   - Many of those refusing to opt for basic skills training said they did so because of their fear of classrooms and/or reliving the failures of their school days.
>   - Many prisoners complained of the difficulties in going straight because even building work required the passing of a basic test and almost everything required the filling in of application forms or passing of theory tests. They couldn't even apply for benefits without admitting they needed help.
> - THE ASSESSMENT of prisoners demonstrated that:
>   - Overall, 53% of (2,029) prisoners at Chelmsford during the project were diagnosed as having dyslexia, compared to 10% of the UK population (data: British Dyslexia Association).
>
>   Jackie Hewitt-Main, 2012

Here is the study of dyslexia in jail, by Jackie Hewitt-Main. She undertook interviews with all 2,029 prisoners at Chelmsford Prison. She discovered that:

- Before the project started, 60% of the incoming prisoners opted to do neither work nor training for fear of revealing their illiteracy.
- Many of those refusing to opt for basic skills training said they did so because of their fear of classrooms and/or reliving the failures of their school days.
- Many prisoners complained of the difficulties in going straight because even building work required the passing of a basic test, and almost everything required the filling in of application forms or passing of theory tests.
- They could not even apply for benefits without admitting that they needed help [61].

Furthermore, the assessment of prisoners demonstrated that, overall, 53% of (2,029) prisoners at Chelmsford during the project were diagnosed as having dyslexia, compared to 10% as a national norm.

Revealingly, and a key component of the framework I derive in this chapter, anxiety and shame seem to be dominating the prisoners' responses.

4.2 Why Children Fail

> ## Why Children Fail

This brings me on to 'Why Children Fail'. To get to the bottom of this toxic learning failure, we need once more to go back to theory, to see further by 'standing on the shoulders of giants' as Isaac Newton put it.

The giants in education whom I particularly admire are John Holt and Maria Montessori. The giant of neuroscience is none other than Martin Seligman, whom I have already introduced for his pioneering work on Positive Psychology, but actually made an exceptional contribution to the science of learning. I start with John Holt.

4.2.1 John Holt on why children fail

John Holt (1923-1992)

- "Most children in school fail.
  - They fail because they are afraid, bored and confused.
  - they're bored with the meaningless work
  - scared of being punished or humiliated
  - and confused by the fact that most teaching progresses from abstract concepts to concrete examples instead of – as would be more sensible – the other way around.
  - In essence I'd realized, from observing and teaching, that school is a place where children learn to be stupid!"
    How Children Fail (1964)
- If we taught children to speak they'd never learn!
  Teacher Bill Hull (cited in How Children Fail)

Holt wrote an all-time classic on seeing children as individuals. His work is now less influential than it was owing to what I see as the brutalist micro-management approach to education now in vogue. He went on to alienate many educationalists by arguing that formal schooling was essentially destructive and advocating home schooling. But every educationalist should read this book. My view is that the individualization now feasible through individual apps and knowledge sharing finally provides us with the tools to get the best of both worlds [62].

But let's see what he says.

"Most children in school fail. They fail because they are afraid, bored and confused. They're bored with the meaningless work, they're scared of being punished or humiliated, and confused by the fact that most teaching progresses from abstract concepts to concrete examples instead of - as would be more sensible - the other way around. In essence I'd realized, from observing and teaching, that school is a place where children learn to be stupid!"

He also gives this great quote from his colleague, Bill Hull.

"If we taught children to speak they'd never learn!"

4.2.2 Ron Davis: Trigger words and confusion

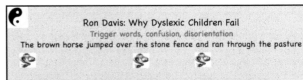

Ron Davis: Why Dyslexic Children Fail
Trigger words, confusion, disorientation
The brown horse jumped over the stone fence and ran through the pasture

- Let's look at a 10 year old dyslexic child trying to read aloud
- The first word 'The' causes the mental imagery to go blank, because there was no picture for it. A blank picture is the essence of confusion... Using concentration however, the child pushes past the blank picture and says 'the' and forces himself to skip to the next word
- ... [concentrating hard he reads 'brown horse jumped over']
- The next word, another 'the' causes the picture to go blank again. Confusion for the reader has increased, but the threshold of confusion has not yet been reached
- ... [concentrating hard he reads 'stone fence']
- The next word, 'and', blanks out the picture again. This time the threshold of confusion is reached and the child becomes disorientated. ... his dyslexic symptoms will appear ...

I also provide an extended quotation from Ron Davis, whose classic book 'The Gift of Dyslexia' highlights not only the gifts of dyslexia, but also the traumas. Davis wrote the book from his own personal perspective as a successful dyslexic. And it has idiosyncrasies, especially regarding his very controversial remediation approach, but he makes a range of priceless observations that deserve enduring consideration [22].

The key ideas here are trigger words, confusion and disorientation. Almost all the dyslexic adults I talk to say - yes, that's me.

Consider this extended quotation. It relates to a 10 year old dyslexic boy trying to read aloud the sentence:

The brown horse jumped over the stone fence and ran through the pasture.

"The first word 'The' causes the mental imagery to go blank, because there was no picture for it. A blank picture is the essence of confusion... Using concentration however, the child pushes past the blank picture and says 'the' and forces himself to skip to the next word.

{So 'the' was a trigger word for confusion}.

... [concentrating hard he reads 'brown horse jumped over']

The next word, another 'the' causes the picture to go blank again. Confusion for the reader has increased, but the threshold of confusion has not yet been reached. Another trigger word.

... [concentrating hard he reads 'stone fence']

The next word, 'and', blanks out the picture again. This time the threshold of confusion is reached and the child becomes disorientated. ... his dyslexic symptoms will appear."

I will now move on to provide the science behind this acute observation in terms of trigger words, confusion and mental fugue states.

4.2.3 Try it yourself mental trauma

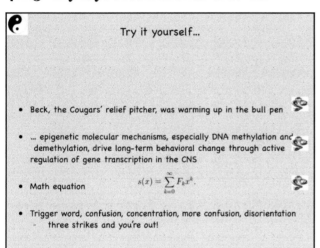

But, first, why don't you try it yourself!?

We all have sources of confusion.

Do you know baseball?

"Beck, the Cougars' relief pitcher, was warming up in the bull pen."

People not familiar with baseball, will be unsure what the Cougars are, what the 'relief pitcher' is, and will have very little idea of what the 'bull pen' is. Their confusion threshold will be reached by that stage.

How about this - which is actually taken from a figure later on:

"... epigenetic molecular mechanisms, especially DNA methylation and demethylation, drive long-

term behavioral change through active regulation of gene transcription in the CNS."

Most of us would actually be doing the equivalent of Davis' boy. 'Epigenetic' - what does that mean? 'DNA methylation and demethylation' - what does that mean? 'active regulation of gene transcription' ... it's too much. You can't get mental traction on it. There are too many things you don't understand.

To move on to math anxiety, how about an equation...

Those of you familiar with math will know that this means 'function s of x is the sum from k=0 to infinity of F subscript k times x to the power k'. But for most of us it's going to be just a trigger for confusion and math avoidance.

So we get trigger words, confusion, concentration, more confusion, disorientation - three strikes and you're out! You have lost mental traction, you just tune out.

4.2.4 Mathematics Anxiety

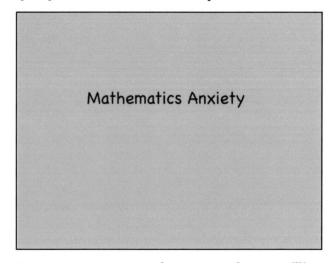

For some reason, researchers are much more willing to consider math anxiety than reading anxiety - somehow it is more acceptable to be anxious about mathematics than reading. So here is some recent research on math anxiety.

4.2.5 Dyslexia and Arithmetic

> ### Dyslexia and arithmetic
>
> - Literacy and Numeracy are the two foundation skills that underpin school success. For some reason there is a greater tolerance of numeracy failure
> - There is a high overlap between dyslexia and dyscalculia
> - Need for automatization
>   - Numbers
>   - Number bonds (8 + 5 = 13)
>   - Number tables (6 x 7 = 42)
>   - → mental resources needed even for simple calculations
>   - → less resource available to work out what to do
> - But many (non-dyslexic) fluent readers are poor at mathematics. Why is this?

First, it is worth highlighting that dyslexia is actually highly associated with arithmetic problems. Literacy and Numeracy are the two foundation skills that underpin school success. For some reason there is a greater tolerance of numeracy failure. But there is a high overlap between dyslexia and dyscalculia.

Numbers need automatization much the same as reading. We need to know our number bonds, that 8 add 5 is 13 and 6 times 7 is 42. If we don't know that, most arithmetic is too resource-intensive. Mental resources are needed even for the simple calculations. So there is less resource available to work out what to do.

One can therefore understand why dyslexic children might be poor at math. But many (non-dyslexic) fluent readers are poor at mathematics. Why is this?

4.2.6 Mathematics Anxiety

> ### Mathematics Anxiety
>
> - Extensive recent research.
> - "math anxiety [is] present at the beginning of formal schooling, which is much younger than was previously assumed ... Perhaps most striking, many of the techniques employed to reduce or eliminate the link between math anxiety and poor math performance involve addressing the anxiety rather than training math itself". Maloney & Beilock (2012 p.405)
> - "It is remarkable that cognitive information-processing deficits arising from math anxiety can be traced to brain regions and circuits that have been consistently implicated in specific phobias and generalized anxiety disorders in adults". Young, Wu & Menon (2012 p.500)

Math anxiety then. There has been extensive recent research.

"Math anxiety [is] present at the beginning of formal schooling, which is much younger than was previously assumed ... Perhaps most striking, many of the techniques employed to reduce or eliminate the link between math anxiety and poor math performance involve addressing the anxiety rather than training math itself" [63].

"It is remarkable that cognitive information-processing deficits arising from math anxiety can be traced to brain regions and circuits that have been consistently implicated in specific phobias and generalized anxiety disorders in adults" [64].

> ### Math Anxiety 2
>
> - More girls than boys show a math anxiety trait
>   Goetz et al. (2013)
> - When anticipating an upcoming math-task, the higher one's math anxiety, the more one increases activity in regions associated with visceral threat detection, and often the experience of pain itself (bilateral dorso-posterior insula). Interestingly, this relation was not seen during math performance, suggesting that it is not that math itself hurts; rather, the anticipation of math is painful.
>   Lyons & Beilock (2012)
> - By ignoring the powerful role that anxiety plays in mathematical situations, we are overlooking an important piece of the equation in terms of understanding how people learn and perform mathematics.
>   Maloney & Beilock (2012)

More girls than boys - the opposite way round to dyslexia - show a math anxiety trait [65].

"When anticipating an upcoming math-task, the higher one's math anxiety, the more one increases activity in regions associated with visceral threat detection, and often the experience of pain itself (which is the bilateral dorso-posterior insula). Interestingly, this relation was not seen during math performance, suggesting that it is not that math itself hurts; rather, the anticipation of math is painful."

"By ignoring the powerful role that anxiety plays in mathematical situations, we are overlooking an important piece of the equation in terms of understanding how people learn and perform mathematics" [66].

So it is the math anxiety that causes the problems - it is rather like the anticipation of pain, or even a phobia.

4.3 The Dark Side: Acquired Learning Disability

The Dark Side
Acquired Learning Disability

This brings me onto the Dark Side.

I started with the distinction between green field learning and brown field learning. I have built the idea that adverse experiences lead to anxiety, and that this anxiety is a core component of the brown field in which dyslexic children learn to read. But what effects does anxiety have on learning?

Back to Martin Seligman's breakthrough research on learned helplessness, but first a brief explanation of how memory works...

4.3.1 State-dependent and Context-dependent memory

State-dependent Memory and Context-dependent Memory

- The purpose of memory is to 'remind' you of what to expect (and what to do) in a given situation
- Our memories are stored together with the external context and also the internal context (state) in which they occur, and when (parts of) those contexts occur in future, they automatically 'trigger' the memories relevant to that context
- Also relevant to music, smoking, drink, illness, stress, depression...
- Triggering by state plus context is particularly powerful
- It's the dark side that we need to worry about. The way that a context can trigger only negative memories.

The purpose of memory is to 'remind' you of what to expect (and what to do) in a given situation. The way memory works is by using state-dependent and context-dependent cues for triggering related memories.

We are all familiar with, say, a fragrance that reminds us of a particular situation - for me, aniseed and a specific country walk. That is context-dependent memory.

Our memories are stored together with the external context and also the internal context - the state - in which they occur, and when parts of those contexts occur in future, they automatically 'trigger' the memories relevant to that context - like my aniseed memory.

But this is also relevant to music, smoking, drink, illness, stress and depression [67].

For drink, there is extensive evidence that alcoholics have state-dependent memory. When they have had a few drinks, they hide bottles of whisky etc, and genuinely can not remember having done so when they are sober again, but the next time that they are in an inebriated state, they recall what last happened in that state, and retrieve the bottles. Their friends just cannot believe that they genuinely have no memory when sober, but it is a simple consequence of state-dependent memory. An example of triggering by both state and context.

Unfortunately, the same happens for depression. When you are down, because of state-dependent memory you tend to retrieve memories that first happened when you were last depressed, which are almost always depressing, so you get more depressed.

The trick is to change your state so that you are happy. Easier said than done, but the techniques of Positive Psychology derive much of their power from the ability to change mental states.

Similarly for anxiety. When anxious you remember things that happened when you were last anxious, a vicious circle.

This is the dark side that we need to worry about. The way that a context can trigger only negative memories. I hope you notice the word 'trigger' has triggered your memory for the Davis trigger analogy.

I hope this analysis has cast some light on the dark side!

4.3.2 Learned Helplessness

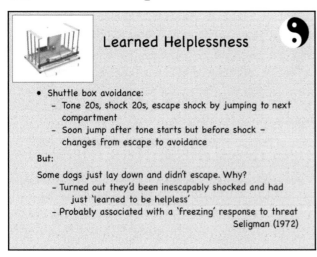

- Shuttle box avoidance:
  - Tone 20s, shock 20s, escape shock by jumping to next compartment
  - Soon jump after tone starts but before shock – changes from escape to avoidance

But:

Some dogs just lay down and didn't escape. Why?
  - Turned out they'd been inescapably shocked and had just 'learned to be helpless'
  - Probably associated with a 'freezing' response to threat
    Seligman (1972)

Let me move on now to Learned Helplessness. This is the Seligman studies with dogs. Seligman and his colleagues used a 'shuttle box', as shown here. The box has two halves, separated by a low, easily jumped hurdle. One half has metal bars on the floor through which an electric current can be directed. If the dog is standing on that side, it would therefore get shocked [67].

In Seligman's shuttle box avoidance approach the dog hears a tone for 20 seconds, and is then given a shock for 20 seconds. The dogs quickly escape the shock by jumping to the next compartment, and soon they learn to jump immediately after the tone starts but before they get the shock, so their response changes from escape to avoidance.

But some dogs just lay down and didn't escape. Why was this? Seligman looked through the records and it turned out they had been inescapably shocked and had just 'learned to be helpless'. This is probably associated with a 'freezing' response to threat.

4.3.3 Fear conditioning - lifelong effects

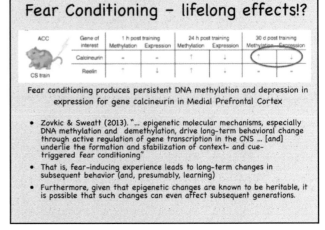

Fear conditioning produces persistent DNA methylation and depression in expression for gene calcineurin in Medial Prefrontal Cortex

- Zovkic & Sweatt (2013). "... epigenetic molecular mechanisms, especially DNA methylation and demethylation, drive long-term behavioral change through active regulation of gene transcription in the CNS ... [and] underlie the formation and stabilization of context- and cue-triggered fear conditioning"
- That is, fear-inducing experience leads to long-term changes in subsequent behavior (and, presumably, learning)
- Furthermore, given that epigenetic changes are known to be heritable, it is possible that such changes can even affect subsequent generations.

Inescapable shock therefore leads to learned helplessness - a sort of 'freeze' response. But it's worse, much worse.

This figure presents the latest neuroscience on what is actually going on in the brain at neural level when these aversive events take place.

This is a study of fear conditioning in rats. The fear conditioning situation is essentially the same as for learned helplessness. The rat is put in a cage, it suffers inescapable foot shock paired with an auditory tone, and fairly soon the poor rat is conditioned to associate the tone itself with the fear of being shocked - whether or not it is shocked. The study is the source for my 'anxiety triggering' quotation a few figures back!

So fear conditioning produces persistent DNA methylation and demethylation, and depression in expression for the gene calcimeurin in the Medial Prefrontal Cortex.

"... epigenetic molecular mechanisms, especially DNA methylation and demethylation, drive long-term behavioral change through active regulation of gene transcription in the CNS ... [and] underlie the formation and stabilization of context- and cue-triggered fear conditioning."

Putting it simply, fear-inducing experience leads to long-term changes in subsequent behavior - and, presumably, learning. Furthermore, given that epigenetic changes are known to be heritable, it is possible that such changes can even affect subsequent generations.

4.3.4 Stress and Learning

Stress and Learning

- Our brains work by a combination of two major systems, sometimes working together, sometimes in competition
  - Declarative system – facts, language-based, available to consciousness, thinking - mind-based learning
  - Procedural system – doing, habits, 'automatic' processes - brain-based learning
- Stress shifts processing to the brain-based action-based procedural system – fight or flight – and indeed reduces blood supply to the declarative circuitry (Schwabe, 2013)
- So even relatively mild stress causes all of us to 'batten down the hatches' and blights any ongoing declarative learning processes
- This could lead to particularly adverse consequences for dyslexic people because it shifts them from their stronger to their weaker learning system

This analysis raises the issue of the effects of stress on learning. We have seen that high levels of fear / anxiety / stress (I am using these terms pretty interchangeably) lead to highly aversive reactions, leading to behavioral responses of learned helplessness, which are underpinned at the brain level by long-lasting and probably irreversible epigenetic modifications.

But there is more. We now have some understanding of how mild versions of these situations actually affect the brain circuits involved in learning.

Let me remind of you of the difference between the two major learning systems, declarative and procedural.

The declarative system is facts, language-based, available to consciousness, and thinking - I have called it mind-based learning in Chapter 3.

The procedural system is for doing, the habits, the 'automatic' processes - the brain-based learning.

The coral on the left corresponds to the stress-free situation - the brain is completely open to learning and is reaching for it with all its might.

But stress shifts processing to the brain-based action-based procedural system - the fight or flight - in order

to escape from that situation, as one would expect. And indeed it reduces blood supply to the declarative circuitry [68].

The effect of stress on learning is like the coral on the right, which has completely closed down. Even relatively mild stress causes all of us to 'batten down the hatches' and blights any ongoing declarative learning processes, because we have switched to our procedural, habit-based learning, for the fight or flight.

This could lead to particularly adverse consequences for dyslexic people because it shifts them from their stronger - declarative - neural system - to their weaker - procedural - learning system.

And so, for dyslexic people, it is as though the anxiety causes their learning capabilities to scrunch up like a hedgehog, or that coral on the right.

4.3.5 Traumatic Stress and Learned Toxicity

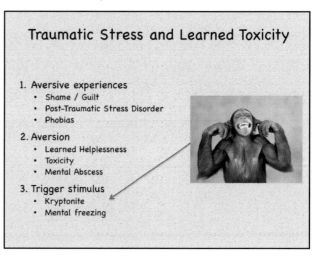

Traumatic Stress and Learned Toxicity

1. Aversive experiences
   - Shame / Guilt
   - Post-Traumatic Stress Disorder
   - Phobias
2. Aversion
   - Learned Helplessness
   - Toxicity
   - Mental Abscess
3. Trigger stimulus
   - Kryptonite
   - Mental freezing

Putting these ideas together, we have a complete (and grim) picture of the effects of stress on learning and mental well-being, which I designate as learned toxicity.

There are various forms of aversive experiences. It could be failures - social, school, family etc. - which lead to a feeling of shame or guilt. Or it could be an overwhelmingly stressful single event like a car accident or something really traumatic at school. Or it could be phobias, like spider phobias, some initial feeling that somehow gets magnified through experience.

If the situation is sufficiently aversive, or sufficiently long-lasting, then we will get an aversion, which may well be associated with learned helplessness, toxicity, and what I call a 'mental abscess'. Furthermore, there are trigger stimuli (such as the sight of a spider) that have been consistently associated with the aversion, which act as kryptonite to Superman, destroying all powers of learning.

The main effect of these triggers is a brain-based situation-escape reaction which is often mental freezing, but might be a fight or flight response.

4.4 Learning Preparedness

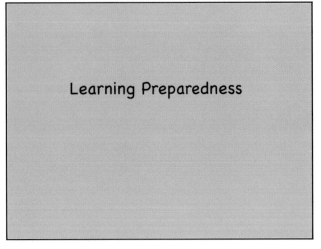

I am nearly there with the theory. Let me just turn to Learning Preparedness. I started with the distinction between green field learning and brown field learning. I have built the idea that adverse experiences lead to anxiety, and that this anxiety is a core component of the brown field in which dyslexic children learn to read. I have revealed the catastrophic effects that anxiety has not just on learning at one moment but all subsequent attempts to learn in that context.

But why do dyslexic children suffer from this anxiety whereas others do not?

I think Martin Seligman's additional breakthrough research on learning preparedness gives us the answer. This is pretty tricky. By all means skip it at first encounter!

4.4.1 Seligman's work on learning preparedness

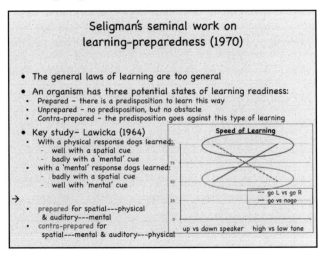

This is again a long time ago - 1970. This work by Seligman helped to finally sink the behaviorist approach. For many years psychologists had puzzled over why they could get pigeons to peck, but not to push a bar with their feet, whereas rats were really good at bar pushing, but no good at nose pushing. And why one could train a dog to do almost any action, but it was much harder to train a dog to do nothing [69].

Seligman demonstrated that the general laws of learning are too general, and that an organism has three potential states of learning readiness:

- Prepared - there is a predisposition to learn this way

- Unprepared - no predisposition, but no obstacle

- Contra-prepared - the predisposition goes against this type of learning.

All vertebrates are wired up for the three fundamental procedural learning abilities - statistical learning, reinforcement learning, and trial-and-error learning, as described in chapter 3.

In addition, different species are wired up from birth with some species-specific learning abilities. For pigeons, it's pecking (and flying!), for rats it's bar pressing, using whiskers and avoiding poison. So far so good.

But you cannot get something for nothing. The downside of this learning preparedness is that if an animal is pre-wired to specialize in one ability, it will make it harder to learn some other task - it is contra-prepared for that task.

Consider this study in dogs by Lawicka 50 years ago. The task was to find food, which was cued by a tone and was in one of two cages. The tone was either a high speaker versus a low speaker (which is a spatial separation) or a high frequency tone versus a low tone (which is more like a mental separation).

The response was either to go to the left hand box or the right hand box (which is a physical action) or to goto the only box versus not going to the box (which is a mental action) [70].

These are the results - basically a dissociation depending on the exact type of response and the exact type of stimulus.

- With a physical response (go left vs go right) the dogs learned well with a spatial cue (high speaker vs low speaker) but badly with a 'mental' cue (high frequency vs low frequency).
- Whereas with a 'mental' response the dogs learned badly with a spatial cue but well with a mental cue.

This means that dogs were prepared for spatial---physical and auditory---mental but contra-prepared for a spatial cue and a mental response or for an auditory cue and a physical response.

My apologies for the complexity of this study. I expect you may have got some learned toxicity on this - that in fact your confusion level has been exceeded, and you've tuned out! I will try to explain simply...

4.4.2 My interpretation

Putting it simply, dogs are prepared to make a physical response to a physical cue, and a mental response to a mental cue. They are contra-prepared to make a mental response to a physical cue, or a physical response to a mental cue.

Updating the neuroscience context to the present day, I propose that the problems arise because of the need for cross-talk between the declarative (the mental) system and the procedural (the physical) system, the neural circuits.

4.5 Why do dyslexic children fail to learn to read?

So what has this got to do with dyslexia? I have outlined the research on anxiety, on learned helplessness, and on learning preparedness and contra-preparedness. I am going to put this together with my own research on delayed neural commitment to make the case that:

(i) we are contra-prepared for reading;

(ii) this therefore requires considerable preparation;

(iii) dyslexic children take much longer to build the underlying neural circuits;

(iv) they therefore fail initially and repeatedly.;

(v) this triggers reading-context-dependent learned helplessness effects that I label mental abscesses;

(vi) this destroys their ability to learn in the reading context.

4.5.1 What needs to happen for fluent reading?

> ## What needs to happen for fluent reading?
>
> - **Automatize sub-skills**
>   - Letters, Grapheme-to-phoneme, Orthography, Word fixation
>   - Speech internalization
> - **Develop mature executive function**
>   - Learning by being told, attention, working memory, response inhibition, sensori-motor integration
> - **Co-ordinate sub-skills**
>   - Predictive eye movements, Eye-voice span
>   - Lexical look-up
> - **Build and rebuild the necessary neural circuits**
>   - Phonological circuit
>   - Visual Word Form Area
>   - Circuit building, Circuit coordination, Circuit myelination

First, let me just go through what needs to be in place for fluent reading. This is an analysis I presented in the previous chapter, but here the context is how much of this is 'prepared' and how much 'contra-prepared'.

Consider the sub-skills shown in the figure. First one has to automatize these sub-skills - Letters, Grapheme-to-phoneme translation, Orthography, Word fixation, Speech internalization. A letter is a spatial representation, but does not correspond to a physical object. We are completely contra-prepared for such an entity. The differences between letters are spatial but require a mental representation. Contra-prepared. The letters need to be named - spatial to mental/auditory - contra-prepared. We are utterly contra-prepared to learn the sounds of letters!

Most executive functions are contra-prepared - learning by being told, in a classroom without any chance to take turns is completely contra-prepared, from birth and also through the experience of turn-taking at home with mother. Multi-tasking is contra-prepared - we're really prepared to do one thing at a time. By definition, building neural circuits is contra-prepared - preparation means using the circuits we already have, and then rebuilding the neural circuits that we've already built (at great cost!) is naturally contra-prepared.

So it is now clear why reading is actually so hard for everyone. Reading goes against the grain of the human preparedness system, and therefore needs extended time and much preparation.

4.5.2 How do dyslexic children learn (down-side)?

> ## How do Dyslexic Children Learn (downside)?
>
> - **Delayed Automatization**
>   - Phonemes
>   - Letters
>   - Grapheme -- Phoneme
> - **Weak statistical learning**
>   - Don't 'just pick up' phonological regularities (rhymes etc)
>   - Don't 'just pick up' spelling regularities
> - **Delayed Neural Circuit Building**
>   - Hard to acquire the neural circuitry allowing cross-talk between the declarative and procedural circuits
>   - Hard to acquire the visual control to fixate letters in sequence
>   - Hard to acquire the circuit for 'fixate, recognise, translate, say' - and it remains resource-intensive
>   - Hard to acquire the necessary executive control circuits

Unfortunately, all this contra-prepared learning is a nightmare for the dyslexic brain.

This is an adaptation of the findings from Chapter 3, on the downsides of Delayed Neural Commitment. Dyslexic children have delayed automatization for phonemes, letters and Grapheme -- Phoneme translation. They have weak statistical learning, and do not 'just pick up' phonological regularities and rhymes, and do not 'just pick up' spelling regularities.

Furthermore, there is delayed neural circuit building. It is hard to acquire the neural circuitry allowing cross-talk between the declarative and procedural circuits. It is hard to acquire the visual control to fixate letters in sequence. It is hard to acquire the circuit for 'fixate, recognize, translate, say' - and it remains resource-intensive. It is hard to acquire the necessary executive control circuits.

And now this idea of preparedness and circuit building gives a good example and understanding of why this is. The dyslexic children are going to have difficulties at almost every stage of the reading process.

4.5.3 Creating a 'Mental Abscess' - the Toxic Cycle

And so there will be repeated learning failures - what I call the Toxic Cycle. And this is a key figure.

A learning failure leads to what I call a 'mental scratch' - it is probably learning failure linked only to the specific context.

If we have repeated mental scratches this leads to what I call a mental lesion, which leads to extended learning failure, linked to the sum of the contexts and will trigger further failures - don't scratch a lesion!

But if we do have further failures - these mental lesions - they will lead to what I've called a 'mental abscess', which leads to pervasive learning failures and affective trauma linked to the broad context.

There is a terrible danger that the learned helplessness caused by this will not only persist as a 'mental abscess', inhibiting learning, but will also 'fester', generalizing to other aspects of the school environment, so that the very thought of school will trigger feelings of learned helplessness and/or helpless rage, for which the only solution is either 'freezing' or actions such as disruption or truancy.

The danger is that a dyslexic child is 'brain-washed' such that the printed word triggers a feeling of learned helplessness or rage, from which there is no escape.

4.5.4 Trigger words and dyslexia

This gets me back to Ron Davis, the trigger words and dyslexia. Davis produced a list of over 200 'trigger words' which induce a feeling of confusion and disorientation, leading to rapid learning failure

Of the 16 most frequent words in the English language 'a and he I in it my of that the then to with' - almost all of them - are triggers, with only 'is was went' not in Davis' list. So 13 were triggers and 3 were not.

Davis advocates the 'symbol mastery' approach to gain automaticity for all 52 letters, then the punctuation marks and other symbols, then the 218 trigger words. He advocates a multi-sensory, game-based automatization approach.

There is clear commonality between Davis' analysis and the neuroscience that I described as leading to a mental abscesses. Davis is trying very hard to avoid these mental abscesses by using multi-sensory game-based approaches. But I believe that the situation is even more perilous than Davis described, in that repeated confusion, leading to repeated disorientation, will lead to learned helplessness - and worse - in the context of reading.

4.5.5 Implications of the learning difference

Implications of the Learning Difference

- At any stage in the process of learning to read, dyslexic children will suffer a 'triple whammy' – less automaticity, weaker phonology and orthography, and delayed executive function
- They will therefore be unable to 'consciously compensate' for all three deficits.
- They will therefore fail to learn, leading to mental scratches
- Perseveration with a formal teaching strategy runs the danger of creating a pervasive mental abscess which prevents learning in a literacy situation
- This may generalise to all formal schooling, with catastrophic consequences
- This is, in effect, an acquired learning disability, resulting from the school experience – considerably more debilitating than math anxiety

The implications of the learning difference are that at any stage in the process of learning to read, dyslexic children will suffer a 'triple whammy' - less automaticity, weaker phonology and orthography, and delayed executive function.

They will therefore be unable to 'consciously compensate' for all three deficits. They will therefore fail to learn, leading to mental scratches.

Perseveration with a formal teaching strategy runs the danger of creating a pervasive mental abscess which prevents learning in a literacy situation. This may generalize to all formal schooling, with catastrophic consequences.

This is therefore, in effect, an acquired learning disability, resulting from the school experience and considerably more debilitating than math anxiety.

4.5.6 Why is reading different from speaking

So, why is reading different from speaking?

- It's a complex skill, built up cumulatively from sub-skills
- The sub-skills are contra-prepared for human learning
  - Especially linking the language system to visual cues without associated actions   *See Toxic learning*
  - There's no 'natural' learning path
  - The units of text are letters and these have no intrinsic meaning
- It's 'brown field' learning rather than 'green field' learning
  - The language system is already in place
  - Need to 'break open' the neural commitments from language to include graphemes
- Acquisition of the sub-skills depends upon 'central' skills that are still developing at age 5-6
  - Executive function
  - Controlled attention
  - Internalized speech
  - Accurate and sustained eye fixation
  - Sequential processing and working memory
  - Coordination of these 'central processor skills'

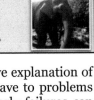

I have derived a pretty comprehensive explanation of why dyslexic children are likely to have to problems in learning to read, and why any early failures can have disastrous consequences, leading to the creation of mental abscesses which have catastrophic effects on subsequent learning in that context. But given these difficulties, why is it that the process of learning to speak is relatively straightforward?

Reading is a complex skill, built up cumulatively from sub-skills. The sub-skills are contra-prepared for human learning - especially linking the language system to visual cues without associated action. There is no 'natural' learning path. The units of text are letters and these have no intrinsic meaning.

It is 'brown field' learning rather than 'green field' learning - the language system is already in place and so we need to 'break open' the neural commitments from language to include graphemes.

Acquisition of the sub-skills depends upon 'central' skills that are still developing at ages 5-6 - executive function, controlled attention, internalized speech, accurate and sustained eye fixation, sequential processing and working memory, and the coordination of these 'central processor skills'.

I have tried to illustrate the central executive trying to control the rest of the brain via the image of the girl on the elephant - the central executive needs to be much better established before the child has to actually use it.

In conclusion, the reason that reading is difficult whereas speech is natural is that reading involves the brown field learning rather than the green field learning, together with contra-prepared skills rather than pre-prepared learning.

4.6 Conclusions on Failing to Learn

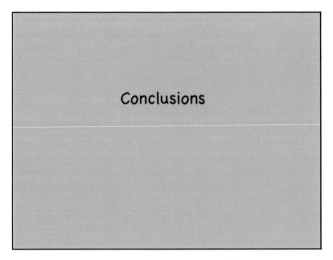

I have covered a lot of ground, including 40 years of the cognitive neuroscience of learning (and its problems), together with the affective neuroscience of learning, and the problems of dyslexia. It is time to wrap up the chapter.

4.6.1 Ontogeny to Adulthood: Drowning not flying

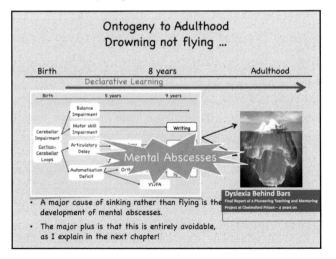

This is the diagram I presented as the Conclusion to Chapter 3. Decreased efficiency in the processes of automatization and brain-based learning leads to

difficulties in reading, writing and spelling at the age of 10 years.

Despite this, some children go on to be highly successful (even if scarred), whereas others go on to have significant problems, with a disproportionate number in prisons.

My explanation relates to the formation of mental abscesses. It is likely that all dyslexic children have mental abscesses, triggered by the reading context.

Some children will actually overcome the problems, or will find a coping response that allows them to minimize the difficulties.

For some there will be a 'freeze' response which will lead to ongoing reading problems, but if it does not generalize to other aspects of school this may not be too serious.

Others will have the mental abscesses, which are the major cause of sinking rather than swimming. There will be a 'fight or flight' response, leading to disruption or truancy. These children will be at significant risk of learning failure and even life failure, with increased likelihood of school problems, offending and a downward spiral.

The major plus is that this is entirely avoidable, as I explain in Chapter 5.

4.6.2 Conclusions to Chapter 4

Positive Dyslexia insists that we allow everyone to work to their strengths, but to achieve this goal we must first avoid catastrophic failures. We must lift the anchor.

Fluent reading requires substantial 'invisible' learning, including the development of the necessary underlying neural circuitry.

Dyslexic children are delayed in creating and consolidating the necessary circuits, and therefore have to make impossible demands upon their cognitive resources. The resulting failures will lead to toxic experiences, resulting in 'mental abscesses' that prevent learning in formal instructional environments and may be associated with 'helpless anger'.

In some individuals this helpless anger will lead to truancy, delinquency, offending, in others a range of displacement activities, in others a complete disengagement. In these cases, the children have learned to fail, and we have, in effect, created the learning disability.

If we had dyslexic people designing our education it would be in very much better shape.

Those are the conclusions of a pretty grim chapter. I have been dwelling on the barriers to progress, the anchor that stops you getting under way. The dark side.

And a very dark side it is - the delays in aspects of cognitive development characteristic of dyslexia are compounded by impatient teaching techniques that actually induce both trauma and learning disability.

Fortunately, the remainder of the book takes the positive side.

This has been another theoretical chapter, this time considering why dyslexic children fail. The results are extremely worrying, suggesting that we may actually have a hand in causing these learning failures, via mental abscesses.

On the other hand, the analysis does show clearly just why reading is so difficult - for all children - and it gives us optimism for thinking that most tasks do not involve that combination of contra-prepared skills and neural networks required for reading. So dyslexic children and adults should very rarely suffer the degree of trauma that they do in learning to read.

Fortunately, I am able to take the positive view in the remaining three chapters - Succeeding in School, Succeeding in Work, and Succeeding in Society.

4.6.3 End of Chapter 4

End of Chapter 4

Chapter 5: Succeeding in School

5.1 Chapter Introduction

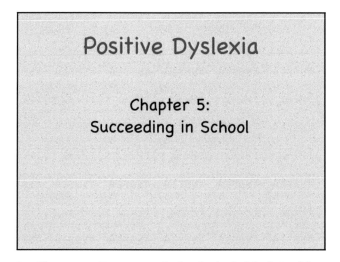

In Chapter 1 I presented the logic behind Positive Dyslexia, the need to work to strengths rather than weaknesses. In Chapters 2 and 3 I considered the strengths of dyslexia - what they are and why they are, ending up with the concept of delayed neural commitment. In Chapter 4 I looked at the down side - why dyslexic children often fail to thrive - and I attributed this to an interaction from a mismatch between teaching methods and the degree of neural and executive maturation, which can cause what I call toxic learning experiences.

In this chapter, I am back on the positive track, as is clear from the title 'Succeeding in School', and I consider both early school, for which there is the possibility of green field learning, and secondary school, where it is necessary to undo the damage caused by previous toxic learning experiences.

5.1.1 The Positive Dyslexia Journey

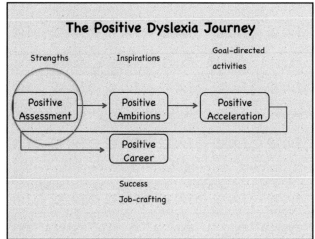

This is the blueprint for the Positive Dyslexia Journey.

There are actually differences depending on the developmental stage. If it is early in life, there is no need to try to find strengths - we know the strengths in terms of natural learning.

This diagram corresponds to the later school, where damage has been done already, and so we need the emphasis on strengths to change the mindset.

Consequently, I have divided this chapter into stages, the prequel, pre-school, early school and late school, because different approaches are needed at each stage.

5.1.2 Plan of Chapter

> ## Plan of Chapter
>
> - Dyslexia the Prequel
>   - Language Learning
>   - Natural Learning
> - Dyslexia pre-school
>   - Preparing the mental ground
>   - Actions not words
>   - Examples
> - Dyslexia in Early School
>   - The importance of systematic reading support
>   - Adapting for dyslexia
> - Dyslexia in Adolescents and Adults
>   - Curing the mental abscess
>   - Rebooting the system
>   - Examples
> - Do's and Don'ts

So, the plan of the chapter is:

- Dyslexia the Prequel;
- Dyslexia pre-school;
- Dyslexia in Early School;
- Dyslexia in Adolescents and Adults.

And I end up with a short series of important Do's and Don'ts.

5.2 Dyslexia the Prequel

> ## Dyslexia: The Prequel

Dyslexia is a challenging learning disability, because it is defined in terms of failure to learn to read, and so cannot formally be diagnosed much before the age of 8 years or so. Nonetheless, dyslexia is normally there from birth, and the reading problem is just the outcome of a series of less critical learning differences.

I will therefore be trying to illuminate the early differences, and of course I will emphasize that we need to understand the theory.

5.2.1 Learning to Speak

> ## Learning to Speak...
>
> - If we taught them to speak, they'd never manage it"
>   Bill Hull (cited in Holt)
> - Why do dyslexic children learn to speak with few problems, even though this might seem the harder task!?

I will start the prequel with the acquisition of language and speech, and remind you of the quotation from Bill Hull which I mentioned in chapter 3, namely:

"If we taught them to speak, they'd never manage it."

Which brings me on to:

Why do dyslexic children learn to speak with few problems, even though this might seem the harder task!?

Fortunately, there has been considerable recent progress in the understanding of how infants do learn to speak, and this provides the platform for my subsequent analyses.

5.2.2 Acquisition of Language

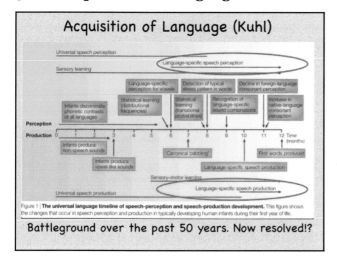

Battleground over the past 50 years. Now resolved!?

This chart - developed by Pat Kuhl and her colleagues in 2004 - represents the current understanding of how speech and language develop over the first year of life [50].

There has in fact been an enormous amount of research on this over the past 60 years, starting with a big debate as to whether in fact there were some sort of human-specific language acquisition device that allowed us to learn our mother tongue. This debate has now been resolved, basically to indicate that the learning abilities required are pretty much the primitive ones that I have already mentioned.

If we look at the green parts - language perception - in the first 6 months, basically any infant can discriminate any of the sounds in any of the human languages.

However, in months 6-12, the infant becomes a specialist in its mother tongue, essentially using statistical learning to identify the regularities of its heard environment.

This leads to good discrimination of the phonemes in its own language, but at the expense of phonemes in other languages. The classic example is the fact that Japanese infants can discriminate /l/ from /r/ at 6 months but lose this ability by 12 months, because the distinction is of no significance in the Japanese language.

Hence we have language-specific speech perception by 12 months.

An equivalent set of processes occurs for the speech production, with general processes occurring in the first 6 months, but gradually in months 6-12 the trial-

and-error learning processes allow the infant to produce the language-specific speech sounds, providing a synergy between hearing and speaking.

Hence we have the language-specific speech production and the language-specific speech perception.

5.2.3 Learning to talk naturally

Acquisition of Language (Kuhl, 2004)

- Statistical (self-organising) learning. This 'tunes' their hearing to their own mother tongue phonology & prosody.
- The innate learning abilities of statistical learning, reinforcement learning, and trial-and-error learning are sufficient to bootstrap the language system, as long as there is an engaging language experience.
- Social interaction with the mother – motherese helps receptive speech development; and turn-taking provides significant advantages for speech production
- Neural commitment creates language-specific speech analysis and production capabilities that are efficient but hard to change.

From my perspective, this figure summarizes the main points.

Statistical (self-organizing) learning 'tunes' the hearing of the infant to its own mother tongue phonology and prosody.

The innate learning abilities of statistical learning, reinforcement learning, and trial-and-error learning are sufficient to bootstrap the language system, as long as there is an engaging language experience.

Furthermore, a key point from Pat Kuhl's work that I have not mentioned in my learning anlsyses so far, is the role of social learning. Kuhl highlights the social interactions with the mother, with the mother using 'motherese' to help receptive speech development; and using turn-taking to provide significant advantages for speech production (and error-dependent learning) [71].

Finally, as the language-specific hearing and speaking skills develop, the underlying neural circuits commit to that processing method. There is no going back. We have reached a brown field language situation!

5.3 Bilingual Learning

I next move to bilingual language learning. More and more children are now learning two languages from birth.

One might think that infants in a bilingual environment would be at a disadvantage, because it is a much more confusing language environment.

But there is some quite startling recent evidence that shows quite the opposite.

5.3.1 Bilingual Language Learning: The advantages of delayed neural commitment...

> **Bilingual Language Learning**
> **The advantages of delayed neural commitment...**
>
> - Bilingual infants take a bit longer to 'neurally commit'
>   - "... bilingual and monolingual infants show a different timetable for developmental change, with bilingual infants remaining "open" to the effects of language experience longer than monolingual infants, a highly adaptive response to the increased variability of language input that bilingual infants experience."
>   - Garcia-Sierra et al. (2011, p. 556)
> - But it's worth it ever after...
>   - Better executive function at 24 months (esp. for Stroop task)
>   - Poulin-Dubois et al. (2011)
>   - Better working memory at 5 (especially when difficult)
>   - Morales et al. (2013)
>   - Better perspective taking at 8
>   - Greenberg et al (2013)
>   - Protection against Alzheimers...
>   - Bialystok et al. (2012)
> - An example of 'premature neural commitment' by monolinguals!

Consider this quote from Adrian Garcia-Sierra, Pat Kuhl and their colleagues indicating that bilingual infants take a bit longer to 'neurally commit': [72]

"... bilingual and monolingual infants show a different timetable for developmental change, with bilingual infants remaining 'open' to the effects of language experience longer than monolingual infants, a highly adaptive response to the increased variability of language input that bilingual infants experience."

I have highlighted in blue on the figure the phrase that I think is particularly crucial for delayed neural commitment for dyslexic people later on.

However, that extra effort to learn the two languages is worth it ever afterwards. They get better executive function at 2 years, better working memory at 5 years (especially when the task is difficult), better perspective taking (that is, better empathy) at 8 years and even protection against Alzheimers at 60 years...[73-76].

In short, 'normal', monolingual children actually have a disadvantage, because they have focused on just one language, and have therefore neurally committed to just one part of the overall game - an example of premature neural commitment. Once one has committed, it is well-nigh impossible to get the same level of fluency for a second language because one is then in a brown-field learning situation. There is already one language hogging all the processing!

5.4 Natural Learning

Children learn to speak and hear language entirely naturally - what implications does this have for learning to read naturally?

We need to look into natural learning.

5.4.1 Forms of Natural Learning

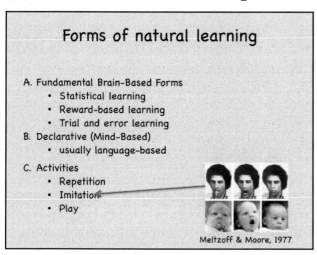

Forms of natural learning

A. Fundamental Brain-Based Forms
- Statistical learning
- Reward-based learning
- Trial and error learning

B. Declarative (Mind-Based)
- usually language-based

C. Activities
- Repetition
- Imitation
- Play

Meltzoff & Moore, 1977

5.4.2 Natural Learning

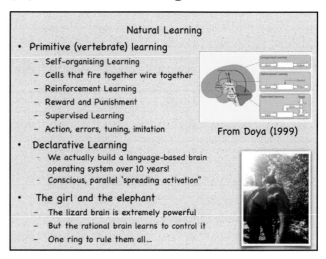

Natural Learning

- Primitive (vertebrate) learning
  - Self-organising Learning
  - Cells that fire together wire together
  - Reinforcement Learning
  - Reward and Punishment
  - Supervised Learning
  - Action, errors, tuning, imitation

From Doya (1999)

- Declarative Learning
  - We actually build a language-based brain operating system over 10 years!
  - Conscious, parallel 'spreading activation"

- The girl and the elephant
  - The lizard brain is extremely powerful
  - But the rational brain learns to control it
  - One ring to rule them all...

Readers who have already gone through chapter 3 will be familiar with these fundamental forms of learning - if not, perhaps you might like to have a look at Chapter 3. We have the set of primitive learning capabilities courtesy of the vertebrate brain - statistical learning, reward-based learning and trial-and-error learning.

But we also have declarative learning, which I call mind-based learning, which is usually language-based and allows us to play with concepts in a conscious fashion.

The activities that are used to develop these skills - especially the brain-based forms - are repetition, imitation and play.

Just to give an idea of the extremely powerful imitation abilities that even a one-day old infant has, this is classic work by Andrew Meltzoff [77], who showed that the infant was able to imitate pretty well the facial actions that he made.

This led the language specialist Michael Studdert-Kennedy to remark, "how does the light get into the muscle!?" That is, the light from the eyes get into the muscle of the tongue? It is now thought that there are 'mirror neurons' that support this sort of action repetition, but even this seems miraculous to me!

So: there are three forms of brain-based learning, one form of mind-based learning, and activities which foster those - repetition, imitation, play. Those are the natural forms.

If we put these various learning concepts together we get the following types of learning - primitive, which is the primitive vertebrate brain. Self-organizing (statistical) learning, cells that fire together wire together - that's the Hebb rule, if two sets of neurons are simultaneously active they tend to join up - it is probably the same event.

Primitive forms of learning include: Reinforcement Learning, Reward and Punishment, and Supervised (trial-and-error) Learning. Much of this learning derives from actions, which allow processes such as error-reduction, tuning, and imitation [78].

And then there is declarative learning - we actually build up a language-based brain operating system over 10 years, and it is conscious, parallel and typically works by spreading activation.

Here I again have the metaphor of the girl on the elephant. The lizard brain - in this case the elephant - is extremely powerful, but the rational brain - the girl - learns to control it. One ring to rule them all as Tolkien would say!

5.4.3 Great Developmental Educationalists

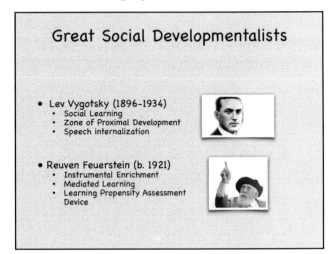

Great Developmental Educationalists

- Maria Montessori (1870–1952)
  - Montessori Schools
  - children's spontaneous activity
  - educator as facilitator of natural development
  - play, exercise, independence

- Jean Piaget (1896–1980)
  - Stages
  - Action-based learning
  - Bricolage

In order to see further, we need to stand on the shoulders of giants. For me these are the giants of educational psychology, each of whom made an extraordinary contribution to the understanding of children's social and cognitive development. Their contributions, unfortunately are no longer as well known as they deserve.

I start with Maria Montessori, who developed a 'scientific pedagogy' in the 19th century, and opened the 'Casa dei Bambini' for mentally retarded children in Rome in 1906. Her ideas focus on using children's spontaneous activities such as play and exercise - their natural ones - to develop independence and initiative. Montessori schools have spread internationally, and perhaps the key ethos is revealed by the role of the educator as 'facilitator of natural development' rather than as 'teacher' [79].

Jean Piaget was the central figure in mid-20th century psychology, having a major role in creating the sciences of developmental psychology and cognitive psychology by his books on cognitive development - which are in turn based on acute observation of his own children's development.

His framework of four developmental stages - sensorimotor to 2 years, pre-operational to 5 years, concrete operations to around 10 years and then formal operations - remains the major attempt to classify the development of a child's cognitive processing ability and has been immensely influential. In addition, he emphasized the fact that without action there is no learning.

Piaget's most evocative idea for me, though, is that of 'bricolage' - which is a French term which means something like 'cobbling a solution together from whatever is to hand.' So the child creates new ideas and skills by adapting the existing ones. For me, though, the key point that he stressed is that the form of learning has to be appropriate to the child's stage of development.

It is counter-productive to use abstract teaching methods if a child has not reached the formal operations stage. If only current educators were more familiar with this! [80]

Great Social Developmentalists

- Lev Vygotsky (1896–1934)
  - Social Learning
  - Zone of Proximal Development
  - Speech internalization

- Reuven Feuerstein (b. 1921)
  - Instrumental Enrichment
  - Mediated Learning
  - Learning Propensity Assessment Device

The Russian psychologist Lev Vygotsky, who died in his thirties from tuberculosis, left a legacy highlighting the social dimensions of child learning, and provided a perfect complement to Piaget's emphasis on cognitive development.

For me, the two other contributions that are particularly powerful are his ZPD - at any age, there are some concepts that a child can learn if the learning is scaffolded by another - this is the ZPD - the zone of proximal development. If the teacher identifies a child's ZPD and acts appropriately, this can lead to exceptional and lasting progress.

Vygotsky also realized the importance of internalizing speech to form the basis of thought, an achievement that has not been well enough followed up, and I think is very important to understand reading [81].

Finally, we need to recognize the enormous contribution of Reuven Feuerstein, who was trained in the Piagetian school, and worked in the then newly-formed state of Israel with children with profound learning difficulties. He discovered that it was possible to intervene very effectively with such children, creating amazing changes. He introduced a range of innovative approaches, including the Learning Propensity Assessment Device (which is an assessment system) and Instrumental Enrichment (which is an intervention system) based around the information from the LPAD.

Most recently, his approach is described as 'mediated learning' in which the educator acts to 'mediate' the learning by adapting the teaching methods to the child's level and interests [82]; [83].

I hope you can see that, much as the Positive Psychologists found when they surveyed the world's enduring philosophies and religions, that although there are significant differences between these approaches at the detail level, there are common themes emerging from all of these approaches (and indeed for John Holt, whom I mentioned in Chapter 4).

I put forward my take on this in the next figure.

5.4.4 The Learning Spiral

I have created this analogy that I call the learning spiral, with the bottom of the spiral corresponding to birth, and perhaps each complete rotation corresponding to a year, with many steps in between.

These six characteristics - which I've culled from the various educationalists whom I have just mentioned - seem to me to provide the core requirements for natural learning:

• Social because we are designed to work with others - for young children it has to be a small group, maybe one or two or three;

• Immersive because we need to be a part of the environment to learn;

• Playful because that takes away stress and facilitates learning

• Personal because that way we are making sure it is grounded and of relevance to the learner;

• Experiential because we need ideally to have a combination of experiences and actions that allow learning by trial and error;

• Repetitive - repeated on the day (to facilitate trial-and-error and statistical learning) and also occurring over several days (to allow overnight consolidation and then refreshing).

The closer we can make the learning environment to these six - SIPPER - the better.

One cannot rush learning - if you have not built the steps you cannot keep climbing - it has be progressive!

Furthermore, the role of the 'teacher' is not to teach, but, as Einstein said, to support. "I never teach my pupils. I only attempt to provide the conditions in which they can learn."

5.5 Dyslexia Pre-school: Implications for Support

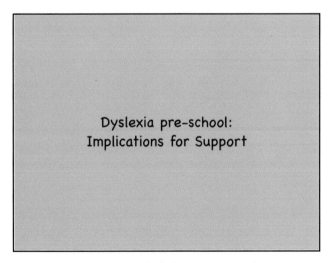

We now have an underlying conceptual structure from cognitive / developmental pedagogy. What does this mean for dyslexic children - or technically, pre-school children who are likely to get diagnosed as dyslexic in a few years given teaching-as-usual?

5.5.1 Reading Activities and Sub-Skills

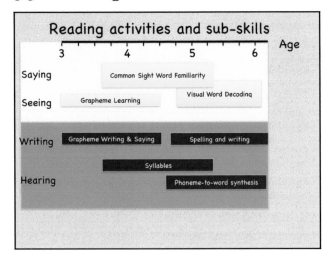

This schematic gives an overview of the general stages in early reading acquisition, based on the model of Uta Frith in the 1980s. You will see this chart follows a similar layout to the one I showed earlier (§5.2.2) for the process of language acquisition [84].

I have divided it into four learning channels - saying, seeing, writing and hearing. I will go through the yellow ones first.

First we need to learn the letters - I have labeled them graphemes.

Next there is learning of a few frequent words, which are recognized as a unit - it might start with a company logo, and then perhaps a word perhaps mum, dad, the child's name. These are recognized as a unit without any realization that the units are made from individual letters. Frith calls this the logographic stage.

Next - and this is the start of sophisticated reading - each word is recognized as a sequence of letters, and is decoded into that letter string. Frith calls this the alphabetic stage.

In parallel with this seeing and saying, there are writing and hearing requirements.

First we need to be able to write the letters, because these actions help make the link between the abstract visual representation and the abstract sound.

Next we need to be able break a spoken word down into syllables.

Then, in coordination with the decoding skills, we need to be able to build up the word from the individual letter sounds - the synthetic phonics stage. This is scaffolded by spelling and writing the words letter by letter and by mentally combining the phonemes into the word - /c/ /a/ /t/ makes /cat/.

5.5.2 Orton-Gillingham Method

Orton-Gillingham Method

- The Orton-Gillingham multi-sensory method for teaching of reading (Gillingham & Stillman, 1956) stresses the need for simultaneous use of all three 'learning channels', namely visual, auditory and kinesthetic-tactile.
- June Orton made the interdependency clear, citing the two basic principles as:
  - Training for simultaneous association of visual, auditory and kinesthetic language stimuli – in reading cases, tracing and sounding the visually presented word and maintaining consistent direction by following the letter with the fingers during the sound synthesis of syllables and words.
  - Finding such units as the child can use without difficulty in the field of his particular difficulty and directing the training toward developing the process of fusing these smaller units into larger and more complex wholes.

  J. Orton (1966, p. 131) cited by Henry (1998, p. 11).

How do the classic dyslexia approaches fit in with this framework? I will start with the first systematic method for teaching dyslexic children. This is the Orton-Gillingham method named after Samuel Orton, the pioneer of dyslexia research and practice in the USA and Anna Gillingham, an educator.

And this is its strength. The Orton-Gillingham multi-sensory method for teaching of reading stresses the need for simultaneous use of all three 'learning channels', that is the visual channel, the auditory channel and the kinesthetic-tactile channel.

As June Orton notes here, there is a very clear interdependency. The two basic principles are:

"Training for simultaneous association of visual, auditory and kinesthetic language stimuli - in reading cases, tracing and sounding the visually presented word and maintaining consistent direction by following the letter with the fingers during the sound synthesis of syllables and words.

Second, finding such units as the child can use without difficulty in the field of his particular difficulty and directing the training toward developing the process of fusing these smaller units into larger and more complex wholes" [85].

There is also a comprehensive and flexible manual, highlighting the need to suit the intervention to the particular pattern of difficulties shown by the individual learner, which has been substantially updated over the years.

But why do Orton and Gillingham stress multi-sensory learning, whereas current best practice tends to focus primarily on phonological processing? For this we need to go back to the theory I developed in the previous chapter.

5.5.3 How to help dyslexic children learn

> ## How to help dyslexic children learn
>
> - Preparation and Inoculation
>   - So that the appropriate sub-skills are scaffolded and learned successfully without trauma
>   - Age-appropriate natural learning
>   - Especially for contra-prepared skills
> - Enrichment
>   - Use of methods for adding meaning and game element
> - Immersion
>   - Daily exposure
>   - Family involvement and scaffolding
> - Patience!
>   - Much easier to do harm than good
>   - Don't force, remember delayed neural commitment

This figure gives what I consider to be a reasonable summary of how we can mediate the learning of dyslexic children. It works the same whether the children are dyslexic or not, it is just that dyslexic children show delayed neural commitment, and also have more difficulties unlearning bad habits.

So, we start with Preparation and Inoculation. The key link here to the theory is the idea of contra-prepared skills. And the key advantage of multi-sensory learning is that it bridges the contra-prepared link between vision and audition, as I will discuss in the next figure. Also we need Enrichment - use of methods for adding meaning and a game element.

Next, for natural learning we need Immersion as with the child's language learning - daily exposure, family involvement and scaffolding via other everyday activities.

And we need above all Patience! It is much easier to do harm than good. Do not force, remember delayed neural commitment.

5.5.4 Inoculation

> ## Inoculation
>
> - Term from Seligman – build up resilience
> - Create an environment in which dyslexic children (or those at risk of dyslexia) are able to develop the skills and attributes needed to overcome the difficulties they will have when starting to learn to read
> - Relate to personal experience
> - Learn by 'osmosis'
> - Use mnemonics to help learn letters before school
> - Manual control practice

Let me just go back to Inoculation. I think this is the key for these early learning experiences. Inoculation comes from Martin Seligman's analysis - it is a method of preventing the mental abscesses being created by undertaking age-appropriate, enjoyable activities that build the structures necessary for successful reading [86].

A key element of inoculation is to create an environment in which dyslexic children (or those at risk of dyslexia) are able to develop the skills and attributes needed to overcome the difficulties they will certainly have when starting to learn to read.

These four activities build towards inoculating against learning failure:

- Relating to personal experience;
- Learning by 'osmosis' - just naturally from what the child already knows and from its environment;
- Using mnemonics to help learn letters before school - because that is a declarative skill;
- Manual control practice, to reduce the mental resources needed for writing.

5.5.5 Positive Dyslexia Pre-School

Positive Dyslexia Pre-School

- Fluent reading depends upon mastery of a range of subskills, starting with spoken language, then knowledge of the alphabet, then the link from graphemes to phonemes.
- Knowledge of the alphabet involves contra-prepared non-natural learning.
  - The alphabet letters are abstract visual representations of the sounds that make up words
  - the child has no understanding that words are divisible into sounds.
- The child should therefore master the letters of the alphabet without directly associating them with words.
  - Letterland makes it easier to remember the individual letters.
  - Orton-Gillingham action-based, multi-sensory approach
- The trigger words should also be mastered as indivisible units, as should say the 100 most frequent words in children's books. This is a relatively simple task for a learner with the power of a 4 year old child. A Chinese child has to learn 800 symbols by the age of 8...
- Written language should be introduced in a natural way
- Examples of the opportunities with apps follow

This figure provides more detail and general guidelines on the inoculation processes.

Fluent reading depends upon mastery of a range of sub-skills, starting with spoken language, then knowledge of the alphabet, then the link from graphemes to phonemes.

Unfortunately, knowledge of the alphabet involves contra-prepared, non-natural learning. The alphabet letters are abstract visual representations of the sounds that make up the words. They have no correspondence to real world objects. The child has no understanding that words are divisible into sounds.

So, in my view, the child should therefore first master the letters of the alphabet without directly associating them with words.

Letterland makes it easier to remember the individual letters. The Orton-Gillingham action-based, multi-sensory approach also does this.

The trigger words should also be mastered as indivisible units, as should say the 100 most frequent words in children's books. Actually, this is a relatively simple task for a learner with the power of a 4 old child. A Chinese child has to learn 800 very confusable symbols by the age of 8...

Written language should be introduced in a natural fashion.

This is easier said than done you might say. And this is where I think the power of apps transforms the playing field.

5.5.6 Example of Early Letter Learning: Play with Mummy

Example of Early Letter Learning: Play with Mummy

Here I try to give some concrete examples of how these processes can indeed be scaffolded. I have written some simple apps - more as a proof-of-concept than as working apps - but I hope that skilled app makers will take on the challenge and turn them into superbly motivating fun games.

I will start with the letters, which are a major impediment for many children, not just dyslexic children. So here is an example of early letter learning - Play with Mummy.

My Letter Actions App

My Letter Actions App

- **b** is for buzzy bee. He buzzes towards the flower, stops and drinks some nectar, then buzzes around in a circle looking for some more.
  – Like this...
  – Can you help buzzy by tracing along the path...

- **d** is for danny dog. He likes to play fetch. Can you see here he's next to you, he goes round in a circle, you throw the ball and he dashes after it, brings it back, and drops it for you.
  – Like this...
  – Can you help danny by tracing along the path...

This is the 'My Letter Actions' app. The core idea is to

scaffold the contra-prepared association by means of actions that are prepared for each part.

Letterland and other alphabetic learning environments are effective because they make a link between the shape of the letter and its name

But I think we can do better. We can make a link between the shape of the letter, the way to write it, and its name. In this case the action of writing the letter (on say a touch-sensitive tablet) is a prepared action. Equally, the idea of acting out a story is a prepared ability. So the tracing action makes the bridge between the contra-prepared linkage.

Have a look at /b/ and /d/ in the figure. These are visually confusable letters, which are left-right reversible, a major problem for dyslexic children.

But not with this system!

- "b is for buzzy bee. He buzzes towards the flower, stops and drinks some nectar, then buzzes around in a circle looking for some more.

  Like this..."

  The yellow indicator on the b in the figure travels down then up and round in a circle, redrawing the b.

  "Can you help buzzy by tracing along the path..."

The app draws the path for the child to follow on the touch screen, thus associating the drawing action with the story, the letter and (indirectly) the latter name.

- "d is for danny dog. He likes to play fetch. Can you see here he's next to you, he goes round in a circle, you throw the ball and he dashes after it, brings it back, and drops it for you.

  Like this..."

  So he chases round in a circle, you throw the ball, he dashes after it, brings it back, and drops it for you.

  "Can you help danny by tracing along the path..."

I hope you will see that the actual tracing consolidates the link between the abstract visual form and the sound that it makes by also introducing a story which actually gives the sound. Similar stories and actions can be created for all the other letters.

So that is how to remember the letters - and you will see we are actually learning those individually.

5.5.7 Example of Early Reading Familiarization: Watch with Mother

Example of Early Reading Familiarization: Watch with Mother

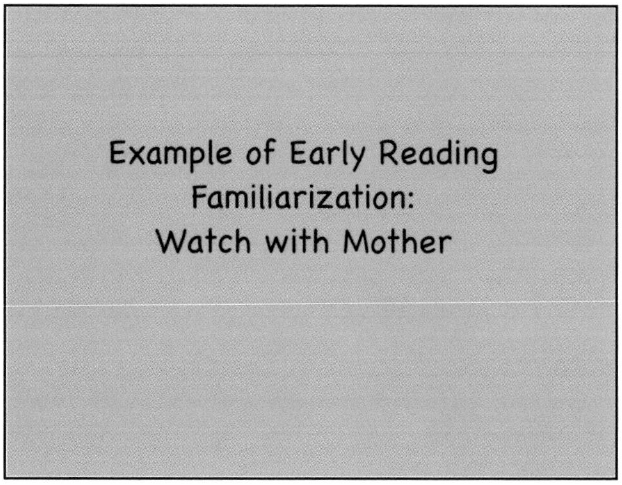

The great educational technology advocate Seymour Papert, who was actually trained in Piagetian techniques, wrote the wonderful book 'Mindstorms: Children, computers and powerful ideas'. Papert was an advocate of natural, immersive learning, and talked of 'Mathland' - what would happen if children who cannot do math grew up in Mathland, a place that is to math as France is to French? [87]

This is my effort to make a ReadingLand, where reading is as natural as talking.

The 'Watch with Mummy' App

The 'Watch with Mummy' app

- Key Features
  - Natural
  - Repetitive
  - Unpressured
  - Seamlessly in everyday life
  - Social
  - Personalised
- My idea is to provide an authoring system - an app maker - so that everyone can build their own

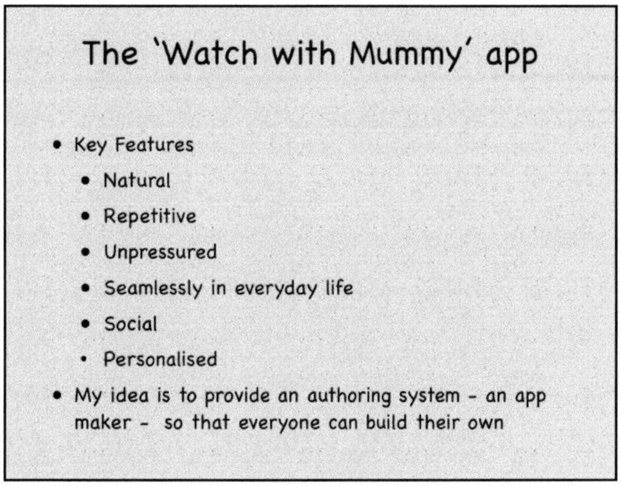

This is the 'Watch with Mummy' app.

The idea that a visual word corresponds to a sound is again contra-prepared. The idea behind Watch with Mummy is that everyone likes to watch a 'facetime' type video about themselves or their family. The app is designed so that the words are presented at the same time as they occur in the video.

There is no pressure, the speech-to-word link is not explicitly 'taught', the child can choose to watch it or not. I will show you the systems shortly.

The opportunities for repetition - the speech to word link which is not explicitly taught (the child can choose to watch the words or not) - allow the statistical learning capabilities to work in a 'quality time' environment. So the key features are that it is natural, repetitive, unpressured, works seamlessly in everyday life, is social and personalized.

And so my idea is to provide an authoring system - an app maker - so that everyone can build their own such systems.

Read-with-Mummy App

The idea here is that many parents have smart phones capable of taking video of their children - or grandmother - which can then be shared with friends and family. What if we adapted this 'videoland' to make a personalized reading land, and made a video album in which the photos actually moved, rather as in the Harry Potter books!?

All that needs to be done to make one's own album is to take a video with commentary, transcribe the commentary, and synchronize the transcript with the video. And that is what my video-album-maker app allows anyone to do.

This is an example of a video album that we made about Vicky's dog Max. Let's have a play through...

We click on the album's button, it opens, this is a page of five photos in Max's album.

We choose the one about Max in the snow. We click on that, the video is then shown. We click on the video. It plays.

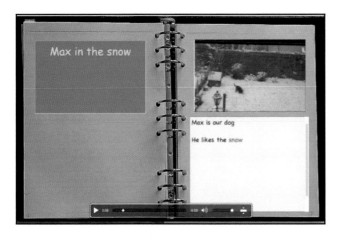

"Max is our dog. He likes the snow." In the app the video plays (and the audio) and the words in the audio appear one after the other with appearance of the words on the screen coinciding with them being spoken

The video continues "It makes him jump. His bone is under the snow. So he digs down to look for it."

And this is the idea: many families take videos and put them in their online album - all we need to do is to allow them to synchronize the audio and the words. And that is what my video album maker allows them to do.

It also lets authors create more interesting reading books of generic interest - like Max's album.

I hope in years to come there will be thousands of these freely available.

5.5.8 Example of Early Reading Familiarization: Read with Mummy

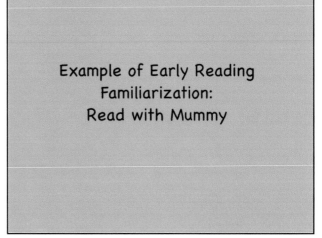

We have developed methods for learning the individual letters, we have developed a statistical learning environment in which the brain can automatically link these units to written words, which are then synchronized with the corresponding speech. This therefore provides excellent scaffolding to support the explicit learning of reading, but we are not yet ready for the ultra-demanding decoding process.

It is time for some whole word learning, which I am calling 'Read with Mummy'.

Sight Word Learning

Sight word learning

- 16 words accounted for a quarter of all words occurring in an 850,000 word corpus:
  a, and, he, I, in, is, it, my, of, that, the, then, to, was, went, with
- 100 words accounted for 53% of the words
- It is therefore possible to design sight word reading apps, including these 100 words, plus words of personal significance, and learn them all by the age of 6
- Young children are 'pre-prepared' to learn by multiple repetitions. Dyslexic children will learn a sight-word very well if
  - it is presented in an enjoyable, accessible, multisensory format
  - the 'reader' experiences immediate feedback and success
  - and for an extended period of time, so that it is overlearned
- These personalised apps, together with interesting, personalised reading books, can be easily created.

My idea here is that we are still - at this age - trying to personalize learning, as though we are just talking to the child, talking about things of importance to him or her, mostly about the family, and things that have happened.

It turns out that some words are much more important and frequent than others. Many of these are the trigger words that Ron Davis identified (as I mentioned in the previous chapter), most are not phonologically regular and therefore do not fit in well with traditional phonics approaches.

I am basing this section on the excellent research undertaken at the University of Warwick by Jonathon Solity and his colleagues.

It turns out, that when one analyzes a huge corpus of words, 16 words accounted for a quarter of all the words in that corpus. And the words were: a, and, he, I, in, is, it, my, of, that, the, then, to, was, went, with. You will see that they are not all regular by any means.

Furthermore, only 100 words accounted for over half of the 850,000 words in the corpus.

It is therefore possible to design sight word reading apps, including these 100 words, plus words of personal significance like the names of family members, and learn them all by the age of 6.

Even young children have rote learning abilities. Dyslexic children will learn it very well if it is presented in an enjoyable, accessible, multisensory format - the reader experiences immediate feedback and success and for an extended period of time, so that it is overlearned.

These personalized apps, together with interesting, personalized reading books, can be easily created.

Imagine if each child already had these words in his or her sight vocabulary by the time phonics instruction starts - they form a solid core of knowledge onto which the new concepts can be grafted and will grow organically, without failure.

5.5.9 Pre-school Summary

Pre-school Summary

- Use only teaching methods appropriate for pre-school children
  - Multi-sensory-motor
  - Personalized
  - Imitation
  - Repetition (but fun and systematic)
- Core requirements of the learning environment
  - Success
  - Enjoyment
  - Repetition
- Best described as *Organic*
  - Growing from within
  - One step at a time
  - Bricolage
- Apps now provide the ideal medium, transforming the educational landscape

I have put all these ideas together for my Pre-school Summary. We have green field learning, and if we get it right, the foundations for easy subsequent learning will be in place.

I advocate teaching methods that match the learning abilities of the child. These learning abilities are primitive but exceptionally powerful.

All four - multi-sensory-motor, personalized, imitation and repetition - are precisely those that allowed the infant to acquire language and speech.

The fourth - repetition learning - was the mainstay of behaviorist education but has been castigated by more modern approaches. It really does have its place as part of a systematic approach, and has the advantage that it taps the core learning abilities of all children. There really is nothing wrong with repetition and success even without great intellectual involvement!

Regardless of learning method there are three requirements for the learning environment. First and foremost, the learner must succeed most of the time.

Second, and equally important, the learner must enjoy it. This is not rocket science! If you do not enjoy it either you will stop or the whole experience will be tagged with the context 'boring', which leads to future problems and possibly mental abscesses.

And Repetition - to repeat myself - is the one that is most often overlooked. The brain needs repetition on the day and from one day to the next, otherwise the necessary neural consolidation does not take place.

If I had to find one word to describe the learning, it is ORGANIC. This is of course literally the case, in that the brain is the organ that is growing to accommodate the new information and skill. It is growing from within. It can only learn one new thing at a time, so make it sure it learns it well, within the right context.

And if we take Piaget's bricolage idea, we build our new skills from the skills and knowledge we already have, like a do-it-yourself builder. Make sure that all the necessary bricks are available - and sound - before trying to build a complicated wall.

Until recently it was well nigh impossible to make these personalized learning opportunities available either to parents at home or to teachers in schools. The educational visionary John Holt was reduced to advocating home education because he believed that schools made children stupid.

But now we can have the best of both worlds. Personalized apps are the disruptive innovation that finally provides the necessary tools.

5.6 Dyslexia in Early School: Implications for Support

Dyslexia in Early School: Implications for Support

Those were my ideas for pre-school, using the powerful primitive learning abilities of the child to acquire the skills needed, scaffolding the contra-prepared linkages with appropriate actions, and enfolding the whole process within a warm cocoon of success, enjoyment and family involvement.

These apps are designed to inoculate the child against the travails that are in store in the early school years.

Let us move on to dyslexia in early school.

5.6.1 Outcomes of the US National Reading Panel Research

Outcomes of the US National Reading Panel Research

- Major investigation over the period 1998-2000 and subsequently
- Investigated effectiveness of different reading programmes at different ages on word decoding, fluency and comprehension
- Main findings were that at the early reading levels, phonological interventions were consistently effective, but they were best augmented by further aspects of reading aimed to develop fluency and comprehension. For older children the value of phonics-based approaches was minimal
- Current consensus: Explicit and comprehensive teaching in alphabetic principle (phonics), vocabulary, comprehension and fluency is needed (Stuebing & colleagues, 2008)
- That is, need to co-ordinate all aspects of skilled reading
- A systematic, well-supported method will out-perform an unsystematic method, whether it's phonics-based or whole word based

It is important to provide a brief overview of the outstanding efforts made in the USA in the late 1990s and subsequently to establish the evidence needed to develop optimally effective reading instruction. This is the US National Reading Panel research [88].

It was a major investigation over those periods and investigated the comparative effectiveness of different reading programs at different ages on word decoding, fluency and comprehension.

The main findings were that at the early reading levels, phonological interventions were consistently effective, but they were best augmented by further aspects of reading aimed to develop fluency and comprehension. For older children the value of phonics-based approaches was minimal.

The current consensus, I think, is that explicit and comprehensive teaching in the alphabetic principle (phonics) is needed, but that also also vocabulary, comprehension and fluency must be included.

In order to read a text fluently, we do not just need to read it, we need to read it and comprehend it. And for this to happen we need to be able to read a phrase within a couple of seconds, because that is the limit of our working memory. We therefore need to build vocabulary, fluency and comprehension, all in a relatively coordinated fashion.

Consequently, the four key requirements are the

alphabetic principle, vocabulary, comprehension and fluency. And they must all be coordinated.

And there is now a consensus that a systematic, well-supported method will out-perform an unsystematic method, regardless of whether it is a phonics-based method or indeed a whole word-based method, it is really important to be systematic and well-supported [89].

5.6.2   Reading Requirements 4-7

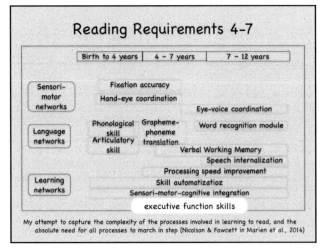

My attempt to capture the complexity of the processes involved in learning to read, and the absolute need for all processes to march in step (Nicolson & Fawcett in Marien et al., 2014)

I will now give my perspective on this. This is my attempt to capture the complexity of the processes involved in learning to read, and the absolute need for all processes to march in step.

On the above chart age increases from left to right - birth to 4 years, 4-7 years, 7-12 years. The language networks are the areas that the National Reading Panel focused on. And it was outstanding given its remit, but in my view it could have significantly enhanced its scope by considering other aspects of the reading process.

The middle row is that analysed by the NRP. Phonological and articulatory skills develop pre-school (though for dyslexic children their phonological skills tend to show considerable delay), explicit teaching then allows the skills of grapheme-phoneme translation (saying the names of letters) develop, then after extensive reading an automatic, a visual word recognition module is created in the Visual Word Form Area (VWFA) which allows the efficient reading of words by sight without the need for laborious phonological decoding. It is also important to develop an efficient verbal working

memory, so that the words just read can be stored for combination with the new ones [90].

But... equally important, in parallel with these language skills, there are also sensori-motor skills and networks that need to be developed. There is the hand-eye coordination needed to be able to write the letters, and (less often considered) there is the binocular gaze control needed to be able to fixate on a single letter in a word for long enough without drifting or jumping. This really is not a skill that is needed outside reading, in that most vision involves a series of relatively under-specified saccades.

But equally important, there is the creation of the necessary brain structures. There is a combination of new circuits - executive function, sensori-motor-cognitive integration, VWFA development - and an increase in automaticity and in circuit efficiency, leading to greater processing speed.

Also, and remarkably little researched, there is the need to internalize speech so that words can be read silently and efficiently.

A key additional requirement, highlighted on this diagram, is the need for the executive function skills to be created during that period between 4 and 7 years.

So any comprehensive theory of reading support - and any comprehensive approach to reading remediation - really needs to take into account this bigger picture of the skills and circuits underlying reading.

5.6.3   Supplementing Systematic Reading Support

Supplementing systematic reading support

- Avoiding the Remedial Reading Group
  - Matthew effects (Stanovich, 1986)
  - Preparation
- Better individual support
  - Individual Education Plans, Response to Intervention
- Use of new technology for reading and writing
  - Touch typing
  - RITA (Nicolson, Fawcett & colleagues, 2000)
  - Dutch reading programme (van der Leij and colleagues, 2013)
  - Jyyvyskala reading programme (Lyytinen and colleagues, 2011)
- Learning by stealth
  - Visual attention (Facoetti and colleagues, 2013)
  - Fitness and exercise (Hillman & colleagues, 2008)

For the pre-school child, the catch-word was inoculation. For the early school child I think the catch-word is supplementation - adding activities that help in the bigger picture of reading

We can rely on the school to give solid phonics-based early reading instruction, so the requirement is to bring all the untaught skills up to speed.

One key requirement is to avoid the Remedial Reading Group, because this leads to slow progress and mental scars. As Keith Stanovich pointed out years ago, we get 'Matthew Effects' in reading. This is a reference to St. Matthew's 'the rich get richer and the poor get poorer' because the better you are at reading, the more you read and the better you get, and the worse you are at reading vice-versa. The key to not being left behind is preparation, but sometimes one needs wider preparation than provided by the school.

A second requirement is better individual support. Schools are run as classes often of 30 children. Teachers do not have the time to do individual assessments. Far too often the individual educational plans are just generic, based on standard approaches, rather than truly individualized, based on insights and experience.

The most exciting, and the most potent supplementation possibilities arise from the availability of new technology. One important skill is touch-typing. This is of course very easily learned these days by means of touch-typing computer programs, often freely available, and extremely effective. I was alerted to the additional value of touch-typing to dyslexic people by the creative dyslexia advocate Richard Wanderman, who pointed out that dyslexic children find writing with a pencil so laborious that they take so much time and effort with the physical act, that they have no spare capacity to comprehend what they have written - or to learn anything. His advice was - learn to touch type as young as possible, it is the gift that keeps giving.

There are also many excellent computer-based reading support systems. A very early example is RITA - Readers' Interactive Teaching Assistant - which provided supplementary exercises in all aspects of reading from phonics to word blending to dictation to comprehension, and could be individually tailored to each child or teacher. More recent systems, deriving from the outstanding initiatives in the Netherlands and in Finland, are the Gramma program developed by Aryan van der Leij and his colleagues in the Netherlands, and the Graphogame (now internationally available) in Finland. These programs have been shown to be very effective [91]; [92]; [93].

Finally, there is the most exciting possibility. Rather than learning effortfully, learning by stealth as part of a game. A good example is the work of Andrea Facoetti and his colleagues. In order to improve covert attention, they used a 'shoot-em-up Raving Rabbids' game in which a key skill was to monitor where the bad rabbits were likely to appear on the screen. The children (who were dyslexic) enjoyed the game, played it a lot, and got better at covert attention and eye fixation, but also they improved significantly at reading [94].

More generally, while computer games tend to improve just the skills they teach (as one might expect) there are some activities that appear to have more general benefits. Chief among these is exercise, which appears to improve not only physical fitness but also mental fitness, and even stimulates the growth of new brain neurons and connections [95].

5.6.4 Early-school Summary

So to summarize the Early-school issues, the key points are as follows.

- Most schools now have systematic approaches to reading instruction. It is crucial to minimize confusion by not interfering with the core reading method used in the child's school.

- Nonetheless it is possible to supplement and elaborate the everyday teaching quite easily.

- Maximize learning by repeating it with the child in

a comfortable environment close to bed-time, and using materials of personal relevance.

- The core requirement is to combat any toxic learning and to emphasize that reading is fun.
- Do not be afraid to use apps and computers to supplement the school approach.

5.7 Dyslexia in Adolescents and Adults: Implications for Support

Dyslexia in Adolescents and Adults: Implications for Support

I have suggested that for pre-school children, the core requirement is inoculation. For early-school children the key requirement is supplementation, so as to ensure that the school-based teaching is indeed effective, and no mental abscesses are caused.

We now move on to later life - dyslexia in adolescents and adults. Here the situation is completely different, and the principles of Positive Dyslexia - finding and developing strengths - come into their own.

5.7.1 Strategy: Dyslexic Adults and Adolescents

Strategy: Dyslexic adults and adolescents

- Here we are working on a 'brown field' site, that is a brain that has already been scarred by previous bad experiences, and indeed will have 'mental abscesses' that can be triggered by specific contexts
- The strategy therefore is:
  - Bypass mental abscesses
  - Use best practice for adults
  - Reconfiguration, Adaptation, Inspiration, Acceleration

Consider the strategy for dyslexic adults and adolescents. Here we are working on a 'brown field' site, that is a brain that has already been scarred by previous bad experiences, and indeed will have 'mental abscesses' that can be triggered by specific contexts.

The strategy therefore is: bypass mental abscesses; use best practice for adults; and then four long words, reconfiguration, adaptation, inspiration and acceleration as I shall explain shortly. But first I will go through theory of best practice for adults.

5.7.2 Andragogy: Best Practice for Adults

Andragogy: Best practice for Adults

- How do adults learn? (Knowles, andragogy)
  - 'Pull' goals rather than 'push' goals
  - Personal significance
  - Immersion
  - Organic
  - Quality Time
  - Success
- See discussion in next chapter
- Follow your star!

How do adults learn best? Fortunately this is an area for which any adult has an intuitive feel, and indeed for which there is a complete literature, andragogy [96].

Andragogy is the study of facilitation of adult learning (as opposed to pedagogy, which is for the children). Malcolm Knowles was the founder of the discipline.

- The key point is that we must be motivated to learn because it is what we want to do, not because we are told to do it. It has to be a pull goal, not a push goal.
- We learn by tackling issues of personal significance to us, often over extended periods of time.
- And we like to learn organically, by adapting what we know already, rather than from square 1.
- We need quality time so that we can get a run at it without distractions and in a positive environment.
- And last but most important, of course, is success. Everyone learns better if they have successes en route.

I discuss this further in the context of Career success in the following chapter, but for the present, the Positive Dyslexia mantra 'Follow Your Star' gives the key principle.

5.7.3 Reconfiguration: Avoiding the Mental Abscess...

(i) Reconfiguration: Avoiding the mental abscess...

- Avoiding the trigger context – don't pick at it!
- Changing the brain state to attenuate the trigger context
  - State change
    - Eating, drinking, music...
  - Cognitive change
    - Relaxation, mindfulness
    - Positive Psychology
    - Learning context (computers...)
  - Incompatible actions
    - Exercise
    - Talking
- Reshaping the brain
  - Building safe walkways
  - Creating escape routes
  - Re-routing the trigger

The first of the four principles is Reconfiguration - which is basically avoiding the mental abscess.

Clearly the easiest way of avoiding the abscess is to avoid the trigger context - reading. If you want the scars to heal, don't pick at them. But that is not a complete answer, we do need to be able to think about reading without breaking into a cold sweat...

So the question is how can we get round the snakes and ladders of life by just going up the ladders and avoiding the snakes!? Which are of course, the trigger contexts.

I have two main suggestions: changing the brain state and reshaping the brain.

Consider first changing the brain state. Here the actions are rather like those of Cognitive-Behavior Therapy for coping with psychological traumas. There are various possibilities, first change the brain's state so that it is not the same as when the mental abscess was caused. We can do this by things you do not do at school such as eating food, drinking coffee, listening to music...

Or we can induce cognitive changes, by relaxation and mindfulness, or by standing up, or lying down. Or we can use Positive Psychology.

Or we can change the context by using computers, or playing music, and so on. All these changes will attenuate the trigger and may give sufficient opportunity to reroute the processing such that it avoids the abscess.

An alternative is to undertake incompatible actions. Exercising causes significant changes in the patterns of blood supply, and therefore causes changes in brain state. Even talking can have a positive effect.

Finally, and most excitingly, there is the possibility of reshaping the brain circuitry so that the mental abscess is healed or bypassed. An example of a safe walkway would be to take an area of intrinsic interest - say football, for boys - and developing the reading around this positive context. The highly successful dyslexic adults surveyed by Rosalie Fink developed their reading skills through their 'passionate interests'.

The escape route is a method of recovering from triggering the mental abscess. It is a method of recognizing the ensuing state and recovering equanimity, another CBT technique.

Re-routing the trigger refers to methods such as the use of tinted lenses so that the visual information is actually relayed to a different part of the visual cortex and therefore bypasses the mental abscess.

5.7.4 Adaptation

(ii) Adaptation

- If a dyslexic child cannot learn the way we teach, we must teach him (or her) the way he (or she) learns
- Optimize the learning conditions
- Mnemonics
- Declarative Learning
- Use new technology
- Touch-typing
- To complement the teaching that is done at school

After reconfiguration, we have adaptation, following the classic mantra.

"If a dyslexic child cannot learn the way we teach, we must teach him or her, the way he or she learns."

As we have seen in Chapter 3, dyslexic children have weak brain-based learning but strong mind-based, declarative, learning.

Hence the general plan is to optimize the learning conditions. If the learning task is a procedural one, try to optimize the conditions by keeping it simple, giving good feedback, building on success, and repetition.

Maybe we can also use mnemonics to change a brain-based task to a mind-based task. Wherever possible, we try to use declarative learning, which is one of the strengths.

Wherever there is a chance, use new technology. It has advantages of immediacy, feedback, motivation, prestige and - especially and positively - change of learning context. I have already mentioned the advantages of touch-typing.

The key point, again, is that must we complement the teaching that is already going on at that school.

5.7.5 Inspiration

(iii) Inspiration

- Set your own goals
  - Pull goals not push goals
  - Resets the context away from toxicity
  - Find strengths and try to work towards them
- Find inspiring role models
  - Inspirational stories of high achieving {dyslexic} adults
  - Whether dyslexic or not
- Build an inspiring social network
  - Inspire and be inspired!
  - Work as a team
- Positive Psychology
  - Wealth of inspirational ideas for everyone
- Do it now! Immediate accessibility (internet)

We now move onto inspiration. This is the heart of the Positive Dyslexia approach, following your star.

Inspiration involves setting your own goals, going for pull goals rather than push goals, resetting the context away from toxicity to positivity, and finding your strengths and trying to work towards them.

A big part of the approach is to find inspiring role models - Richard Branson, Susan Hampshire, Tom Cruise, Jack Horner - who have made outstanding contributions in their chosen careers and can provide the inspiration for the hard work needed to achieve success.

One of the strengths triads we discovered is the social triad of teamwork, empathy and communication, so the key to developing these strengths - and to enjoy yourself - is to build and cultivate a social network, who can inspire you and be inspired by you. The more you enjoy teamwork, the better you get, and the better you can judge people's strengths. These 'soft' skills are the key to work success.

Positive Psychologists have already developed a whole range of valuable techniques and a literature describing them - dip in!

But perhaps the most valuable advice of all for inspiration is 'Do it Now'. And you really can these days, with the internet providing a wealth of opportunities to find all the information and inspiration you need!

5.7.6 Acceleration

> ### (iv) Acceleration
>
> - Try to improve the ability to learn
> - Teach strategies
>   - Especially those related to potential strengths
>   - Mind-maps, emotional intelligence, proactivity etc
> - Make more assertive – avoid confusion
> - Consider brain-based learning
>   - nutrition
>   - 'brain games'
>   - Coordinative Exercise
> - The optimal intervention will be specific to the individual and requires analysis of learning abilities as well as disabilities

Reconfiguration, adaptation, inspiration, now acceleration.

Think how much time you spend learning, and what a difference it would make if you were able to learn just 10% more efficiently. That really is the gift that keeps on giving.

There is a great opportunity to improve learning by using strategies, especially those using your strengths, or potential strengths. Using mind maps to exploit and develop big picture strengths and visual strengths, building emotional intelligence to get help with your teamwork and develop the social triad. Picturing what's likely to happen, and taking actions to make sure it goes well will develop the skills of proactivity and flexible coping.

One of the consequences of difficulties can be a 'freezing' response - keeping your head down, not complaining - learned helplessness. It is really important not to suffer in silence. If you are confused, say so, get help. Confusion is the assassin of learning.

But the major opportunity is that of accelerating the brain-based learning processes, because if they can be improved you will have the best of both worlds. It is often not realized that the brain-based learning processes do change during puberty, and so the storm and stress of adolescence does give a real opportunity.

Sometimes simple changes in nutrition can help, there is evidence that some dyslexic individuals would benefit from additional fatty acids.

There is no doubt that 'brain games' can improve specific attributes - attention, working memory, speed of processing. And I am sure there will be great developments in this area.

One area that seems to me to be of great promise is that of coordinative exercises. There is strong evidence - though not yet in the dyslexia field - that exercise can potentiate the brain for new learning, with coordinative balance exercises leading to neural growth in the hippocampus - a core structure for mind-based learning [97] - and also in the cerebellar-cortical loop [98] - a core network for brain-based learning. Consequently, coordinative balance exercises may prove beneficial both for mind-based and brain-based learning, whether the exerciser is dyslexic or not.

However, everyone is different. Whether dyslexic or not, you need to experiment, to find the learning intervention that works for you. When you do, it will benefit you throughout life.

5.7.7 Goal Mapping

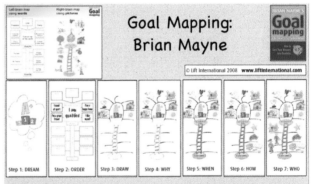

Excitingly, and deserving a larger section here, Brian Mayne's internationally renowned 'Goal Mapping' technique succeeds spectacularly in terms of providing not only an antidote to the mental abscess but also an injection of positivity and a tried-and-tested implementation path for identifying and achieving goals [99].

The map on the top left, taken from his website, indicates the power of the approach. Goal Mapping involves a collaboration between the sequential, rational brain processes (shown on the left) and the intuitive, visualization-based declarative brain (shown on the right).

A key advantage is that not only does the approach allow you to identify and represent your goals, but it also recognizes the importance of developing a clear and inspiring 7 stage action plan to implement them.

I illustrate the process using Brian's template, freely downloadable via his website liftinternational.com.

Step 1: We DREAM – we set ourselves a 'stretch goal', an ambitious target for what we wish to achieve, say in a year's time. The picture here represents the goal of qualifying with a first class mark.

Step 2: Next, ORDER. We identify four subgoals and enter them, plus the main goal, in the sequential, left hand side of the map.

Step 3: We DRAW images to represent the main goal and subgoals on the visual side of the map, the right.

Step 4: WHY – we think carefully why we want to achieve these goals, entering the reasons in words at the top on the left, and in images at the top on the right. These images represent freedom, love and family.

Step 5: WHEN, makes you decide a firm start date and finish date, and enter them on the 'lift ladder' on both sides.

Step 6: HOW, is where you have to confront the details of how you're going to climb that ladder in that time, and is again entered in words on the left and pictures on the right.

Step 7: WHO, is the final step – which other individuals do you need to get on your side to help you to achieve your goals? Again, entered on both sides.

The full map allows you to engage your whole brain in the process, and Brian recommends placing a copy of the map in prominent places where you are re-minded everyday.

Not only does this allow users to avoid any mental abscesses by recruiting more brain regions and flooding with positivity, but it builds on the big picture skills of dyslexia to create a powerful and successful action method for the Positive Dyslexia goal of 'finding and following your star'.

5.8 Teach Them the Way They Learn: Concluding Do's and Don'ts

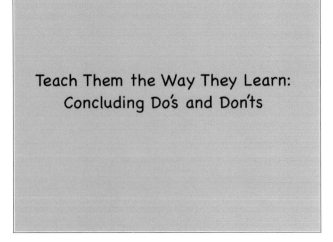

We are approaching the end of this chapter. I have covered a big range very quickly.

For pre-school children I argued that the main task was Inoculation - building up the necessary skills and neural circuits to support formal learning. I suggested that personalized apps could provide the ideal inoculation methods, and illustrated this with natural apps for letters, reading and sight words.

For early school children I argued that the main goal was to Supplement the standard curriculum to ensure that the child keeps up and does not suffer toxic failure.

For adolescents I argued that the main aim was to recover from the toxic failure of early school, and I provided suggestions for Reconfiguration, Adaptation, Inspiration and Acceleration.

5.8.1 Do's

> ### Do's
>
> 1. Create an environment that is qualitatively different from the 'toxic' environment associated with previous learning failure
> 2. Ensure that the new learning environments are associated with positive prestige
>   - Working to strengths (see also the 'Rebranding Dyslexia' chapter
>   - Use of 'new' methods (especially app-based)
>   - Use of high prestige context changers – for example, use of sensorimotor techniques that are associated with top sports
>   - Ensure success
> 3. If these conditions can be met, everybody has a chance to heal (or at least bypass) the mental abscesses that perpetuate learning failure
> 4. Cultivate ambition, the belief that failure can be turned around. The brain changes enormously at puberty, and is always generating new neurons (especially with exercise)

5.8.2 Don'ts

> ### Don'ts
>
> - Do no harm ...
>   - At all costs avoid toxic learning experiences that create 'mental abscesses'
> - If you find you're scratching a mental abscess...
>   - Stop scratching
> - Don't give up - always cultivate the possibility of major success - and don't compound the shame, guilt and confusion already suffered.
>   - many high achieving dyslexic adults speak of some individual who had faith in them and gave them the self-belief to keep going

I will start positively. These are suggestions for children who have already suffered 'toxic' learning failures. These are all do's.

First, create an environment that is qualitatively different from the 'toxic' environment associated with previous learning failure.

Second, ensure that the new learning environments are associated with positive prestige. For example:

- Working to strengths.
- Use of 'new' methods.
- Use of high prestige context changers - for example, use of sensorimotor techniques that are associated with top sports.
- Ensure success.

Third. If these conditions can be met, everybody has a chance to heal (or at least bypass) the mental abscesses that perpetuate learning failure.

Finally, cultivate ambition, the belief that failure can be turned around. The brain changes enormously at puberty, and is always generating new neurons (especially with exercise).

Don'ts. There is only a small list of don'ts, and really they are pretty obvious (though not necessarily observed).

The first commandment is 'do no harm'. At all costs avoid toxic learning experiences that create 'mental abscesses'.

If you find you are scratching a mental abscess - stop scratching. Change the context.

Don't give up - always cultivate the possibility of major success - and don't compound the shame, guilt and confusion already suffered. Many high achieving dyslexic adults speak of some individual who had faith in them and gave them the self-belief to keep going.

5.9 Conclusions on Succeeding in School

Conclusions

- For dyslexic adults and adolescents, damage is already done, and a key requirement is to heal or avoid the mental abscesses
- The principles are given by the Do's and Don'ts in the previous slides, but can be summarised:
  - Use the principles of Positive Psychology to find and work towards strengths. This automatically changes the context from the previous toxic associations
  - Enrich the natural learning abilities with social and computer support. These also change the learning context
  - Be patient, if it's worth doing, it's worth doing properly
  - Generate and celebrate successes – learning is very fragile
- If we had dyslexic people designing our education it would be in very much better shape.

So to conclude this chapter, mostly for adolescents, this is my summary.

For dyslexic adults and adolescents, damage is already done, and a key requirement is to heal or avoid the mental abscesses.

The principles are given by the Do's and Don'ts in the previous figures, but can be summarized:

- Use the principles of Positive Psychology to find and work towards strengths. This automatically changes the context from the previous toxic associations.
- Enrich the natural learning abilities with social and computer support. These also change the learning context.
- Be patient, if it's worth doing, it's worth doing properly.
- Generate and celebrate successes - learning is very fragile.

If we had dyslexic people designing our education system, it would be in very much better shape.

And this concluding statement is not just a throwaway line. I truly believe that our educational system has been designed by and for people with one particular form of talent, the conventional form. Dyslexic people can bring different talents - including the Cognitive Skills Triad and the Social Skills Triad to bear on the issues of education.

Dyslexic designers are particularly attuned to the difficulties of conventional education and have the empathy, the big picture vision, and the creativity to redesign our broken educational system so that it is fit for the 21st century.

In my concluding chapter I argue that the unconventional talents of dyslexic people can re-invigorate conventional industry. Just as important, they can re-invigorate conventional education so that it becomes fit for purpose.

5.9.1 End of Chapter 5

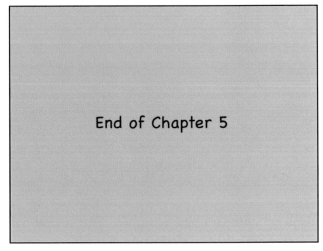

End of Chapter 5

And that is the end of my Chapter on 'Succeeding in School' - the first of the Success Trilogy!

Next I discuss 'Succeeding in Work', then finally 'Succeeding in Society'.

Chapter 6: Succeeding in Work

6.1 Chapter Introduction

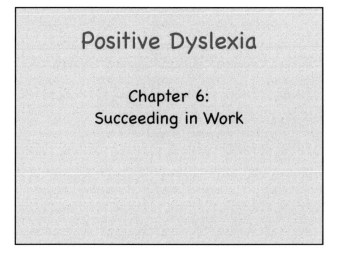

In Chapter 1 I presented the logic behind Positive Dyslexia, the need to work to strengths rather than weaknesses. In Chapters 2 and 3 I considered the strengths of dyslexia - what they are and why they are, ending up with the concept of delayed neural commitment. In Chapter 4 I looked at the down side - why dyslexic children often fail to thrive. And in Chapter 5 I looked at succeeding in school.

Now we have reached one of the least considered but most important areas of dyslexia research, Succeeding in Work.

6.1.1 The Positive Dyslexia 'Blueprint'

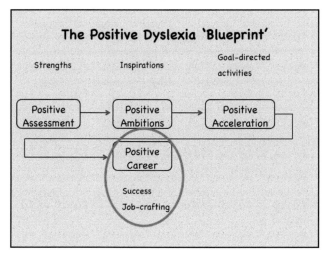

This is the final stage of an individual's Positive Dyslexia journey that I sketched out in the first chapter. We are up to the Positive Career, with Success and Job Crafting.

6.1.2   Plan of Chapter

The plan of the chapter is as follows.

There are four main sections, first methods of finding careers to suit your strengths, then fitting the skills to the career, then the Dyslexia Work Strengths Finder, then succeeding with dyslexia - preparing the ground and crafting the career.

6.2 Careers and Dyslexia

I will first go through the literature on careers and dyslexia. There is not as much as one might expect.

6.2.1 Characteristics of Successful Dyslexic Adults

> **Characteristics of successful dyslexic adults**
>
> - Gerber, Ginsberg, & Reiff (1992). 71 LD students identified from national sample. Key differentiator between successful and less successful was control – both internal and external (social ecologies)
> - Raskind and colleagues (1999, 2003) found similar results – self-awareness, proactivity, perseverance, appropriate goal setting, effective use of social support systems, and emotional stability/emotional coping strategies. These are what I would call 'Work Success attributes' – important for anyone.
> - Agahi, Sepulveda and Nicolson (2014) found the 'dyslexia decathlon' of strengths, with the Work Strengths Triad of Determination / Resilience, Proactivity and Flexible Coping, the Cognitive Skills Triad of Big Picture Thinking, Creativity / Innovation and Visualization, and the Social Skills Triad of Empathy, Teamwork and Communication as described in Chapter 2.

There have been relatively few published studies in this area. I cite three, by Paul Gerber and his colleagues, Marshall Raskind and his colleagues, and the Sheffield studies that I described in Chapter 2.

The Gerber study followed up 71 students with learning disabilities over a period of about 20 years. The key differentiator between the successful and the less successful adults was their level of control - both their internal control and also the control over their external environment, which the authors referred to as social ecologies [100].

Marshall Raskind found similar results (with a similar design), establishing that the successful adults were characterized by self-awareness, proactivity, perseverance, appropriate goal setting, effective use of social support systems, and emotional stability/emotional coping strategies. These are what I would call 'Work Success attributes' - which are important for anyone. But I think it is very likely that they are particularly important for dyslexic adults [101]; [102].

The third set of studies (Sara Agahi, Polly Sepulveda and I) found the 'dyslexia decathlon' of strengths, with the Work Strengths Triad of Determination / Resilience, Proactivity and Flexible Coping, the Cognitive Skills Triad of Big Picture Thinking, Creativity / Innovation and Visualization, and the Social Skills Triad of Empathy, Teamwork and

Communication, as I discussed at length in Chapter 2 [24].

6.2.2 Differential Career Choice in Dyslexia

> **Differential Career Choice in Dyslexia**
>
> 1. Well documented but non-quantitative evidence of a tendency for dyslexic adults to look for careers in creative industries, computing, engineering, architecture, and innovative roles (Eide & Eide, West)
> 2. Wolff & Lundberg (2002). Signs of dyslexia three times as likely in Art students as for rest of University
> 3. Logan (2009). 35% of entrepreneurs show dyslexic traits (as opposed to 1% of corporate managers!)

A further source of information is provided by the sort of careers that dyslexic adults tend to choose - the differential career choice.

It is well-documented that there are relatively high proportions of dyslexic adults working for Google and other West Coast creative industries, and there also seem to be high numbers in computing, the media and architecture, but I have not been able to find and quantitative data on this (although the 'Dyslexic Advantage' and Tom West's books do provide further information) [23]; [18]

One quantitative published study by Ulrika Wolff and Ingvar Lundberg at Gothenberg University found three times the incidence of dyslexic students reading Art than for the rest if the University [103].

A highly cited study by Julie Logan revealed a very much greater incidence of dyslexia in US entrepreneurs, with 35% showing dyslexic tendencies. She also proposed that some of the strategies the entrepreneurs had to adopt to overcome dyslexia (such as task delegation) may be useful in business [104].

6.3 Occupational Psychology: Fitting the career to the person.

Occupational Psychology:
Fitting the career to the person

I have covered a range of disciplines already - Dyslexia, Positive Psychology, Cognitive Neuroscience, Education. They have all provided valuable insights, but the lack of published studies on careers and dyslexia means that it is necessary to bring in a further discipline - careers and occupational psychology.

Occupational Psychology has focused on two main areas: fitting the person to the job, and fitting the job to the person. I consider both of these aspects in this chapter.

6.3.1 Holland Occupational Codes

Holland Occupational Codes

Realistic types prefer to deal with **Things.** [Doers]
tend to be frank, practical, focused, mechanical, determined, or rugged.
Examples: manipulating tools, doing mechanical or manual tasks, or doing athletic activities.

Investigative types prefer to deal with **Things and Ideas.** [Thinkers]
tend to be analytical, intellectual, reserved, independent, and scholarly.
Examples: working with abstract ideas and intellectual problems.

Artistic types prefer to deal with **Ideas and People.** [Creators]
tend to be Complicated, Original, Impulsive, Independent, Expressive, and Creative.
Examples: using imagination and feelings in creative expression .

Social types prefer to deal with **People.** [Helpers]
Tend to be Helping, Informing, Teaching, Inspiring, Counseling, and Serving.
Examples: interacting with people and concerned with the welfare of people.

Enterprising types prefer to deal with **Data and People.** [Persuaders]
Tend to be Persuasive, Energetic, Sociable, Adventurous, Ambitious, and Risk-taking.
Examples: leading, managing, and organizing.

Conventional types prefer to deal with **Data and Things.** [Organisers]
Tend to be Careful, Conforming, Conservative, Conscientious, Self-controlled, and Structured.
Examples: ordering activities, paying attention to details.

I start off by trying to see what sort of jobs are likely to suit dyslexic adults. A well-established approach,

which fits well with our analyses so far and has great face validity, is John Holland's classification of occupational codes, developed in the 1980s. It is a core component to the comprehensive and continually updated O*Net US career choice website. These are the six types [105].

- The Realistic types prefer to deal with Things - they are the 'Doers'. They tend to be frank, practical, focused, mechanical, determined, or rugged. Examples would be manipulating tools, doing mechanical or manual tasks, or doing athletic activities.

- The Investigative types prefer to deal with Things and Ideas - the 'Thinkers'. They tend to be analytical, intellectual, reserved, independent, scholarly. Examples are working with abstract ideas and intellectual problems.

- The Artistic types prefer to deal with Ideas and People - the 'Creators'. They tend to be Complicated, Original, Impulsive, Independent, Expressive, and Creative. Examples are using imagination or feelings in creative expression.

- The Social types prefer to deal with People - the 'Helpers'. They tend to be Helping, Informing, Teaching, Inspiring, Counseling, and Serving. Examples would be interacting with people and concerned with the welfare of people.

- The Enterprising types prefer to deal with Data and People - the 'Persuaders'. They tend to be Persuasive, Energetic, Sociable, Adventurous, Ambitious, and Risk-taking. Examples are leading, managing and organizing.

- And finally, the Conventional types prefer to deal with Data and Things - the 'Organizers'. They tend to be Careful, Conforming, Conservative, Conscientious, Self-controlled, and Structured. Examples are ordering activities and paying attention to details.

6.3.2 Using Holland Occupational Types

To represent the Occupational Types one tends to use the hexagon, as shown above. The layout of the hexagon shows which types are closer to each other. For eample, Conventional is the opposite pole to Artistic, whereas it is quite close to Realistic and Enterprising.

And the way it works is that the users rate themselves in terms of the types, and they pick their top two types and that allows them to find careers with that pair of types.

6.3.3 Holland Occupational Types

Interests assessment						
	Realistic	**Investigative**	**Artistic**	**Social**	**Enterprising**	**Conventional**
Traits	Scientific Mechanical Quiet Reserved Unassuming Practical Nature loving Problem solver Athletic Action/present oriented Common sense Honest	Scientific Analytical Intellectual Inquisitive Mechanical Scholarly Broad interests Precise Thorough Independent Original Future oriented	Broad interests Expressive Dreamy Idealistic Imaginative Intellectual Non-conforming Original Rebellious Sensitive Intuitive	Helpful Enthusiastic Friendly Kind Persuasive Insightful Sincere Trusting Understanding Generous Receptive Sociable Warm	Capable Good leader Assertive Enthusiastic Extroverted Persuasive Power seeking Shrewd Sociable Confident Persistent Adventurous Ambitious	Organised Practical-minded Shrewd Speculative Conforming Conventional Conscientious Efficient Neat Stable Thorough Accurate
Skills and abilities	Mechanical ability Technical ability Athletic ability Using machines Horticulture	Mechanical Intelligent Academic Research Mathmatical Science minded	Artistic talent or knowledge Foreign language ability Design ability	Interpersonal Teaching Training Social Educational Leadership Selling	Leadership Selling Promoting Educational Business Clerical Interpersonal Public speaking	Record keeping Statistics Clerical Business Scheduling Mathematical

So here is an example of the Holland Occupational Types. This is taken from the excellent 'Psychology Student Employability Guide' by Caprice Lantz [106].

It is pretty straightforward. Users put ticks in the boxes they consider appropriate, then count up the

category with the most ticks. You can see those along the top, we have Realistic, Investigative, Artistic and the other three, and so the users get the type with most ticks and then their number 2, then 3. And that gives their top three preferences.

6.3.4 O*Net

1. US job-seekers resource
2. Very powerful

A key reason for using the Holland job types is that the approach has been incorporated in the mammoth O*Net US jobseekers free resource, available to all at onetonline.com.

It is a very powerful system.

6.3.5 O*Net Categories

Occupational Type	Skill Level	Goal
Realistic	JOB ZONE 1 (Little or No Preparation Needed)	Achievement
Investigative	JOB ZONE 2 (Some Preparation Needed)	Independence
Artistic	JOB ZONE 3 (Medium Preparation Needed)	Recognition
Social	JOB ZONE 4 Consid'ble Preparation Needed)	Relationships
Enterprising	JOB ZONE 5 (Extensive Preparation Needed)	Support
Conventional		Working Conditions

This illustrates the O*Net structure.

There are basically three dimensions: the Holland type - as shown on the left above - which the user chooses; the skill level, which is also chosen (for example JOB ZONE 1 indicates no skill in the area, up to JOB ZONE 5 which is very highly skilled in that area); and then the user can also specify his or her goals - achievement, independence, recognition, relationships, support and working conditions.

6.3.6 O*Net Interest Profiler

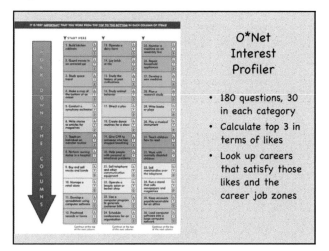

Then the core process is the O*Net Interest Profiler. A part of the whole range of questions is shown above. There are 180 questions, 30 in each of the 6 Holland categories. This allows users to calculate their top 3 Holland job types in terms of their likes. And then they can look up the careers that satisfy those likes, and the career Job Zones.

6.3.7 Example...

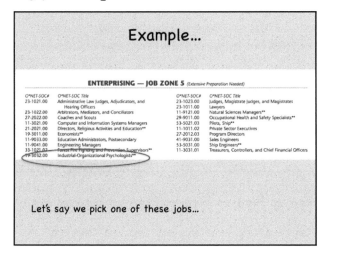

So here is an example. Let us say our Holland type was Enterprising, and we are highly skilled (so Job Zone 5).

Up comes this set of Enterprising Job Zone 5 possibilities, and we pick one of the jobs - shall we say Industrial /Organizational Psychologists. And then we click on that.

6.3.8 Industrial/Organizational Psychology

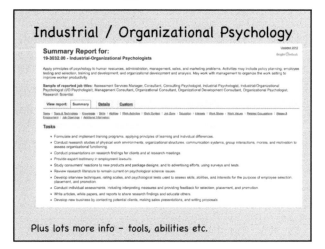

And that takes us to the appropriate webpage, which has masses of information.

The options are probably rather more than most dyslexic adolescents would care for, but it is a terrific resource and allows you to really do a good job of surveying the possibilities.

6.4 Career Strengths

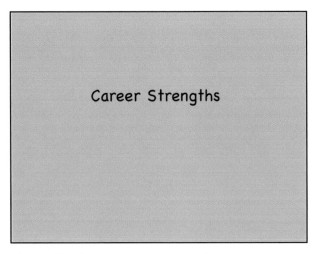

The Holland and O*Net approach is a generic one, applicable to anyone. The question is whether we can actually refine the approach to provide guidance and inspiration that is more specific to dyslexia, and in this section I consider career strengths, and in particular strengths that do not fall into the conventional career framework.

I will start by reminding you of the 10 strengths we identified in Chapter 2.

6.4.1 The 'Strengths Decathlon' of High Achieving Dyslexic People

The 'Strengths Decathlon' was the result of research by Sara Agahi and Poli Sepulveda and me, and we were looking at successful dyslexic adults in conventional careers and entrepreneurs respectively.

We obtained these three 'triads' of skill spanning the whole spectrum.

The cognitive skills triad includes those fundamental, intra-personal skills that have been highlighted by dyslexia researchers - the visuo-spatial skills, including visualization ability; the Big Picture approach, the ability to distinguish the wood from the trees, to get that 'helicopter view'; and creativity and innovation, the ability to think outside the box.

The Social Skills triad is for the inter-personal skills. Here we have Empathy, the ability to see life from others' perspective; Teamwork, the ability to fit well into a team and to help ensure that the team works effectively; and Communication, the ability to explain concepts to others.

Then there is the Work Skills Triad. It is not clear whether all dyslexic people have these skills, it might well be that they are the reason that our interviewees were successful, but there is reason to think that they may well be associated with dyslexia. First, Determination / Resilience. Second, Proactivity, that is thinking ahead to what you might need. And third, Flexible Coping, to think of different solutions to problems.

And I think all of those skills might well have been developing for many years from the school years, where a dyslexic adolescent needs determination and resilience, needs to think ahead, and needs to be able to cope flexibly.

Underpinning these nine strengths is what I have called Unconventional Thinking, which combines the idea of unconventional careers with that of different types of thinking - a less sequential, more holistic, more 'whole brain' approach.

Then there is my theoretical explanation, which I developed in Chapter 3, of Delayed Neural Commitment. This implies strongly that dyslexic adults have the ability to keep learning, keep benefiting from experience, not getting into stimulus-response habits. This underpins many of the developing strengths and gives reason to believe that dyslexic adults will keep learning longer.

I represent the decathlon by this three-pillared temple - with each strengths triad capped off and integrated by the unconventional thinking skills.

6.4.2 Clifton Strengths Finder

Next, let us consider these dyslexia strengths relate to current non-dyslexia strengths approaches. Here are the strengths identified in the Clifton Strengths Finder, which was researched and published by the Gallup organization, and is based on extensive research. There is no particular rationale to the 34 strengths identified, so I have grouped them into categories myself. It has overlaps with the Holland Occupational Types, but also has additional categories of Leader and Competer that go beyond Holland [107].

First, consider the Social category: Communication, Developer, Empathy, Consistency, Positivity, Wooing, Harmony, Includer, Individualization and Relator.

I have put the ones which look dyslexia-friendly in blue.

Then we have the Doer category: the Achiever, the Activator, the Arranger, Discipline, Focus, Deliberative.

Then the Investigator category: Analytical, Connectedness, Context, Ideation, Input, Intellection, Learner, Futuristic.

Again there seem to be quite a few dyslexia friendly strengths there.

And then they have two categories that we had not thought of before, which is the Leader category for the Command, Self-Assurance and the Maximizer. And the Competer, focusing on Competition and Significance.

Looking ahead to the tactics for successful job interviews, it is likely that members of an appointment committee will be familiar with the Clifton Strengths Finder. Consequently, you will surely impress them by saying how you had considered one of your strengths was (say) Ideation, and that you had deliberately developed this strength through study of creative thinking, and that you had specifically chosen their organization because of its reputation for valuing creativity!

6.4.3 Dan Pink: A Whole New Mind

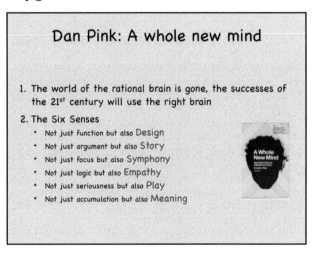

I strongly recommend Dan Pink's book 'A Whole New Mind' [108].

This book is not about dyslexia, but he claims that the intellectual, rational, linear problem solving skills that characterized success in the 20th century are now no longer sufficient. Computers are taking over these functions, and they can also be out-sourced to countries with a highly trained but lower paid workforce.

In his view, the successes of the 21st century will be these softer, more intuitive skills - what he calls the Six Senses. He attributes these to the right brain, but I think this is an oversimplification - I would prefer to say the whole brain. It is not important what part of the brain it is, it is the Six Senses that are. Look at them.

Not just function but also Design, not just argument but also Story, not just focus but also Symphony, not just logic but also Empathy, not just seriousness but also Play, and not just accumulation but also Meaning.

Several of these clearly are very directly related to the dyslexic strengths established in the 'Dyslexic Advantage' - but again, think how you can exploit these strengths in an interview!

6.4.4 Carol Eikleberry

Finally in this section I recommend Carol Eikleberry's book, a Career Guide for Creative and Unconventional People.

This is a tour de force for dyslexic adults (and of course other creative people). It uses the Holland Occupational Types, but it focuses on the Artistic type - which is the opposite pole to his Conventional type. It gets the readers to find their top three Holland types, and gives an inspiring set of unconventional careers for Artistic and any combination of two others.

Eikleberry also recognizes how difficult it is to identify your own strengths and gives these six wise suggestions for how to find out.

Question 1: What are you doing when you are so engrossed you lose track of time? The chances are that it is something you really enjoy.

Question 2: In what kind of activities do you make the boldest choices? The chances are that is when you are most confident - your best skills.

Question 3: What are your occupational daydreams? What would you love to do?

Question 4: Which tasks do you do really quickly? In general the quicker you do it, the more expert you are.

Question 5: What things do you remember best - words, numbers, images? This is a very good question, it gets you to think what your real skills are in those domains.

Question 6: What do people tell you that you are particularly good at? You might as well listen to your friends.

6.5 Towards the Dyslexia Work Strengths Finder

So far, then, I have explained the Holland and O*Net approach, which is a generic one, applicable to anyone, and is more to do with preferences than strengths. I then went through the strengths of dyslexia, and the strengths that are considered important at work, highlighting the match between the dyslexic strengths and the unconventional strengths that Dan Pink suggests are crucial for 21st century success.

The question I look at in this section is whether these dyslexia strengths are actually present before dyslexic people get into careers, and I present the results of a study Sara Agahi and I undertook with University students.

And this was a key component of our ongoing development of the Dyslexia Work Strengths Finder.

6.5.1 Dyslexia Work Strengths at University: Agahi and Nicolson (2014)

> **Dyslexia Work Strengths at University**
> **Agahi and Nicolson (2014)**
>
> 1. In work presented earlier, we have established that:
>   - Successful dyslexic adults tend to show the Big 6 strengths
>   - Entrepreneurs showed these strengths but also benefitted from extended experience in an entrepreneurial environment
>   - We speculate that for many dyslexic adults, their 'Dyslexic Advantage' tends to develop relatively slowly, gaining strength once they have left school and have freedom to develop their strengths
>
> 2. Questions
>   - Are these generalizations true for dyslexic students?
>   - How do the strengths of dyslexic students compare with students in 'specialist' disciplines
>
> 3. Method
>   - Holland plus the Big Six using tests specifically designed to test empathy etc.
>   - Dyslexic students (various disciplines)
>   - Psychology students (Empathy...)
>   - Architecture students (Visuo-spatial...)
>   - Management students (Entrepreneurial skills...)

In work presented earlier (§2.4), we have established that successful dyslexic adults tend to show the Big 6 strengths, that is the Social Skills Triad and the Cognitive Strengths Triad.

Entrepreneurs showed these strengths but also benefited from extended experience in an entrepreneurial environment.

We speculate that for many dyslexic adults, the 'Dyslexic Advantage' tends to develop relatively slowly, gaining strength once they have left school and have freedom to develop their strengths.

So that leads to two questions.

First, are these above generalizations true for dyslexic students? And how do the strengths of dyslexic students compare with students in 'specialist' disciplines?

We developed questionnaires for the Holland plus the Big Six using tests specifically designed to test empathy and so on. And we used Dyslexic students (from various disciplines), and we used Psychology students (predicting they'd be strong on Empathy), Architecture students (predicting they'd be strong on Visuo-spatial skills), and Management students (predicting they'd be strong on Entrepreneurial skills).

6.5.2 Results: Holland Types

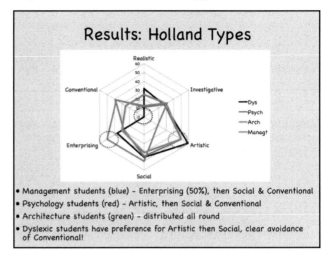

- Management students (blue) - Enterprising (50%), then Social & Conventional
- Psychology students (red) - Artistic, then Social & Conventional
- Architecture students (green) - distributed all round
- Dyslexic students have preference for Artistic then Social, clear avoidance of Conventional!

And these are the results that we found. I have presented the data in terms of a hexagon chart, to correspond to the Holland spatial connectedness. The data are the percentage who placed that category in their top 2 [109].

It is rather hard to follow.

If we look first at the Management students (in blue), 50% of them have chosen the Enterprising category within their top two, and then the two to either side - the Social and Conventional - are their next two choices.

For the Psychology students (in red) Artistic was their top category with 50%, and then Social and Conventional.

The Architecture students (in green) spread reasonably uniformly all round.

The Dyslexic students (in black) have preference for Artistic then Social, and what I have shown here is the ring round the clear avoidance of Conventional - with this sample 0% preferred a conventional career!

6.5.3 Results: Strengths (and weaknesses)

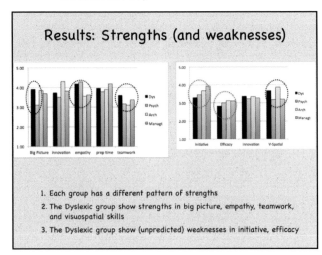

We also looked at the strengths and weaknesses.

The left hand chart indicates their self-assessments on a direct question as to Big Picture, Innovation, Empathy, Preparation Time (which is a measure of Proactivity) and Teamwork (we didn't ask about Communication, unfortunately).

The right hand chart presents the results on published tests of initiative, self-efficacy, innovation and visuo-spatial ability.

You will see that there are clear differences between groups. I will focus on the Dyslexic group. They had significantly higher scores than the Psychologists on Big Picture, and significantly higher scores than the Architects and Management students on Empathy.

So we obtained significant preferences for the Big Picture, the Empathy and also on the Teamwork ratings. There were higher scores than some of the others on those, and also strong scores on Visuo-Spatial.

In summary, the Dyslexic group showed strengths on those aspects that we predicted, but then they also show unpredicted weaknesses on Initiative (these are highlighted in red) and Self-Efficacy.

6.5.4 Conclusions on Study

Conclusions on Study

1. Individual Variations
   - Considerable variability between all students
   - Each student group tended to gravitate towards the expected strengths of that group
   - Whether or not one gets significant differences depends on the dyslexic group and on the comparison group!
2. Support for previous views regarding dyslexia
   - Clear preference for Social and Artistic careers
   - Clear aversion to Conventional careers
3. The dyslexic students have already developed strengths in at least four of the big 6, but not in innovation, and see themselves as lacking in self-efficacy.
4. My view is that these strengths actually develop post-University when the dyslexic students get the chance to work to their own tune, rather than being forced to jump through the hoops of examinations and the like.
5. The DWSF - comprising Holland, the Big 6, and additional tests - is a powerful strengths-based career tool

Our conclusions on the study were as follows. First, as expected, there were huge individual variations, with considerable variability between all students and also within each group. Each student group tended to gravitate towards the expected strengths of that group.

And indeed, whether or not one gets significant differences depends on first the dyslexic group and then on the group with which they are being compared.

But there is support for previous views regarding dyslexia. We did find a clear preference for Social and Artistic careers and a clear aversion to Conventional careers.

And the dyslexic students have already developed strengths in at least four of the big 6, but not in innovation, and they do see themselves as lacking in self-efficacy.

My interpretation of these results is that these strengths actually develop post-University when the dyslexic students get the chance to work to their own tune, rather than being forced to jump through the hoops of examinations and the like.

And the Dyslexia Work Strengths Finder (DWSF) - comprising Holland, the Big 6, and additional tests - is a powerful strengths-based career tool.

6.5.5 Dyslexia Work Strengths Finder

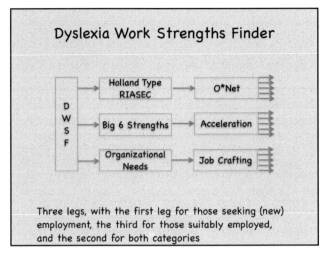

Three legs, with the first leg for those seeking (new) employment, the third for those suitably employed, and the second for both categories

Let us move straight on to the DWSF, which is still in prototype stage. It has three legs.

The first leg, designed for those looking for a career change - is the Holland Occupational Type analyses, leading into O*Net and also other resources such as Carol Eikleberry's suggestions for unconventional careers.

The second leg - suitable both for those in employment and those seeking a change in employer - is direct self-assessments of the Big 6 strengths. The user can exploit this information to see how well he or she matches up to the requirements of the desired job, and gives the psychological impetus and rationale for developing the key strengths further - the acceleration.

The third leg - primarily for those in employment - involves an analysis of the needs of the user's organization, and provides suggestions for job crafting so as to better utilize the strengths found in the second leg.

6.6 Succeeding with Dyslexia at Work

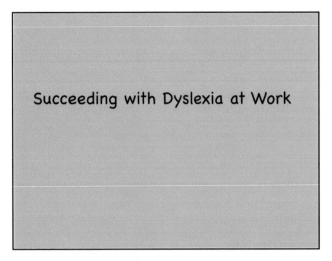

So far, I have covered the literature on work strengths, reminded you of the strengths of dyslexia, and outlined our progress toward the Dyslexia Work Strengths Finder.

This section examines the requirements for Succeeding with Dyslexia at work.

6.6.1 Preparing the Ground

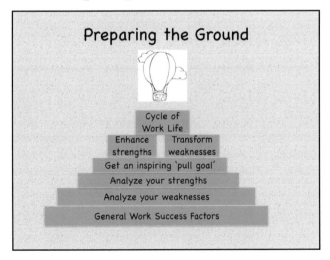

To prepare the ground, I have constructed this pyramid of activities.

Underpinning everything are the General Work Success Factors - which I consider in the next figure.

In common with my approach to Success at School, Positivity alone is not sufficient. Usually it is more cost-effective to improve your weaknesses initially - to raise the anchor before unfurling the sails.

Then strengths analysis, with the intention of getting an inspiring 'pull goal', a job or career you are aiming for (indicated also by the balloon here).

Then you can work on your strengths and your weaknesses.

And the key idea is that by knowing the rules of the game - the Cycle of Work Life - you can craft the interview requirements - the skills, the resumé, your distinctiveness - to your advantage - which is another Dyslexic Advantage, as I show in the next figure.

6.6.2 Work Success Factors

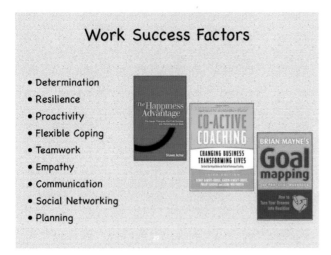

There are of course many general work success factors. Many of these are actually the ones we identified as characteristic of successful dyslexic adults.

In particular, I suggest Determination, Resilience, Proactivity, Flexible Coping, Teamwork, Empathy, Communication, and then a couple more, Social Networking and Planning.

It is obviously not possible in one figure to give a useful overview of what is a vast field, so I will just point out three books I think would justify the effort needed to read them (in this area), by not only providing knowledge but directly turning the knowledge into skills that can be used both for yourself and for others.

I have naturally chosen 'The Happiness Advantage' by Shaun Achor because that has the dual advantage of providing more insight into Positive Psychology while providing important work success ideas [110].

The second choice, 'Co-active Coaching', by Henry and Karen Kimsey-House and their colleagues has a very positive approach and is a good fit to the strengths of dyslexic adults. Furthermore, since a good way to develop a skill yourself is to try teaching it to others, this book also has a dual purpose [111].

Finally, Brian Mayne's technique of 'Goal Mapping', which I described in Succeeding in School (section 5.7.7), provides a powerful and successful way of identifying and achieving goals in work and life, and has outstanding resonance with the whole approach of Positive Dyslexia [99].

So that was the Work Success Factors.

6.6.3 Transforming Weaknesses

This figure is a really important one. It is picking away at that mental abscess, since these weaknesses are those that traumatize dyslexic children at school.

Transforming Weaknesses - Work Smarter and link to your strengths.

The key point is that these weaknesses reflect learning differences, not learning disabilities. For every downside, there is an upside, and the key plan is to work smarter, being aware of, and tolerant to, your weaknesses, so that you can transform them into distinctive strengths. A weakness is a half-way house to a strength.

So, here we have the five horsemen of the apocalypse, as far as dyslexia goes - reading, writing, thinking, rapid processing, and completing tasks. You can turn them to your advantage!

First, Reading. Dyslexic people have problems in terms of speed, memory, effort. Possible solutions include: technology, these days you can use text-speech technology, lots of computer based approaches; a smarter approach; even teamwork, to get people to read key articles quickly for you.

Writing. The problems are speed, accuracy and again effort. Again the solution is technology - voice to text or indeed touch-typing technology - and again teamwork, to actually find a team who can actually help you build your writing strengths and work as a team.

Thinking. The problem here is typically Working Memory, the solution is to use Visual methods - things like Mind Maps.

Rapid Processing. The problem is thinking quickly when 'put on the spot'. The solution is Preparation and Intuition. Preparation involves getting work done ahead of time. Intuition necessitates becoming expert enough to come quickly to a solution.

And the fifth problem, which is not specific to dyslexia of course, but is particularly characteristic, is the problems of Completing a task - organization, time and mental resources.

The solution, I think, is both project management skills (which will be worth their weight in gold for the future) and also for teamwork.

So the 5 horsemen of the dyslexia apocalypse can be turned to one's advantage!

Remember - everyone will encounter these problems, especially when the going gets tougher, so if you have developed strategies to cope with, you will get well ahead. And of course this is a classic way of acing the interview, by saying you had these problems and you fixed them in the following fashion.

6.6.4 Career Development: The Cycles of Work Life

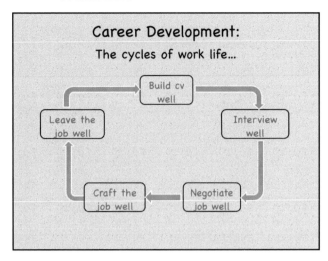

The next two layers of my career success pyramid are analyzing your strengths, and creating an inspiring pull goal. But we can build these into a more comprehensive plan, which I call the cycle of work life.

And here is the Cycle. Build your CV (resumé) well, Interview well, Negotiate your job well, Craft the job well, Leave the job well (if necessary), and then get back to building your CV well again.

If you do want to end up in that perfect job, you need to know the rules of the game, and you need to do some planning. It involves a lot of work, but it will be easy and worthwhile because it is a pull goal! You will not get there immediately, but we have already established that job diversity provides a valuable background resource for creativity!

So these are the stages, as shown above. We start with building the curriculum vitae (the resumé) well.

6.6.5 Building the Curriculum Vitae (Resumé)

> ### Building the curriculum vitae (resumé)
>
> 1. What are my strengths?
>   - Work Strengths, Cognitive Strengths, Social Strengths
>   - MIND Strengths
>   - Experience
> 2. What is distinctive about me?
>   - Dyslexia
>   - Unconventional strengths
> 3. What is the positive evidence?
> 4. {how does it match to the specific job}

The purpose of a resumé is to interest the appointments panel to the extent that they think you stand out enough as a candidate to be worth interviewing.

If you do already know your strengths, you are in a privileged position compared with your competitors. Few people ever realize what their strengths are!

For this purpose, therefore, it is important to highlight your dyslexia because it gives you to the Work Strengths, the Cognitive Strengths, the Social Strengths, the MIND Strengths and your experience.

Often the panel are interested in what is distinctive about you, and that again is where the dyslexia comes in, and the fact that you have unconventional strengths.

And then the third thing that they will always want to know, is what is the positive evidence of this? You need to be able to provide some evidence of these strengths, otherwise the committee will not be convinced. So that gives you a sub-goal - having established your strengths, try to establish evidence. It might be performance on some previous employment, it might be scores on the Clifton Strengths Finder, it could be the DWSF, it could be a personal anecdote. If it is anecdotal it is best not to put it in the resumé, but be ready with it at the interview!

And of course the key idea is to highlight the synergy between your own distinctive strengths and the requirements for doing the job superbly.

6.6.6 Interviewing Well

> ### Interviewing Well
>
> 1. What are they looking for?
>   - Who are they?
>   - What do they do?
>   - Why do they need you?
> 2. Core interviewer goals
>   - Does he/she know what the job is?
>   - Can he/she do it well?
>   - Can he/she do it the way we want?
>   - Will he/she fit in well?
>   - What will he/she add to the team?
> 3. Core interview question
>   - Tell us about a difficulty you have confronted in the past, what you did about it, and what the outcome was
> 4. Key strategy
>   - Get to talk about your strengths (see triads) and experience
>   - Mention the dyslexia – terrific opportunity to take the initiative

So, you have done a great CV, you have got to the interview. It is important to know the rules of the game of interviewing well.

First, try to find out what you can about the job and the panel - the more you can find out, the more you can plan proactively.

The key idea is to put yourself in the position of the interview panel - what are the rules of their game, what are they looking for?

And these five issues capture typical interviewer goals. If you know that this is what they're looking for, you can prepare materials and answers to impress - proactivity should be one of your strengths!

So, what are they looking for? Who are they? What do they do? Why do they need you?

The Core interviewer goals typically follow these five aspects. During the interview they will want to answer these five questions about you, the interviewee:

- Do you know what the job is?
- Can you do it well?
- Can you do it the way we want?
- Will you fit in well?
- And what will you add to the team?

This common set of goals is worth knowing about, and you can see how you can shine by showing how you can add to the team.

The core interview question is "tell us about a difficulty you have confronted in the past, what you did about it, and what the outcome was."

And this very common question is a gift for a dyslexic person - your key difficulty is the effect of dyslexia, so you can provide an anecdote where you had problems owing to say difficulties in reading reams of paperwork in minutes before a meeting, so you took proactive action - for example asking for the information the day before, or at least an executive summary, or you got a friend to summarize - and then were able to make a clear analysis beforehand that was accepted by the Board, and so on.

And this is the key strategy - make it clear that you have real strengths that are the other side of the coin. Just talking about Positive Dyslexia will surely engage their attention and (especially when you have seen the final chapter) make them want to employ you!

There are endless books on interview technique. This book, 'Winning at Interview' by Alan Jones is consistent with the approach I have taken, and is very clear and positive [112].

6.6.7 Negotiating Well

They have offered you the job, well done! You should not just accept, but you should start negotiating. The key is to get your boss (and your colleagues) on your side.

You have already mentioned the difficulties and the strengths arising from your dyslexia, so this is an ideal time to negotiate some adaptations that will allow you - and your colleagues - to perform optimally.

Be absolutely clear about these ideas, and if necessary try to do some extended negotiations to get everything right.

The classic book, 'The First 90 Days' by Michael Watkins gives extremely valuable advice. It is intended for top managers and executives, but the principles apply to everybody [113].

And here are the principles.

- Explain the need sometimes to do things differently, to be judged by results not by methods - not micro-managed.
- Explain how cost-effective it is for you to have a good support environment - everyone working to their strengths, and how this allows good teams to be built up.
- And negotiate with the boss what he/she wants you to achieve in the first 90 days (and subsequently).

6.6.8 Do the Job Well

With any luck, you have negotiated the job well. We are now onto doing the job well. And I think this is a key requirement. If you are failing at the job, you will then be negotiating from a position of weakness.

In your negotiations you should have identified any classic problems that you were likely to suffer (open plan offices, unclear processes, ill-prepared meetings and so on) and agreed a win-win solution with the boss. So, impress the boss with your work, and you will be in credit sufficiently to make some further changes.

The first thing of course is to be sensitive to the boss's needs, plans, goals and pressures. You need to use your skills of proactivity, flexible coping, teamwork and empathy to keep ahead here.

Next, use your skills to develop a positive and distinctive reputation. Your Big Picture skills might let you see what is <u>not</u> being done, your teamwork and empathy skills might allow you to get everyone working more effectively. Being well-prepared for meetings is always noted positively.

In your interview you will have claimed that you have strengths, and that these are associated with dyslexia. Make sure you live up to these strengths. The work triad, the cognitive triad, the social triad.

Look beyond your immediate team - develop your social networks, find colleagues with complementary strengths (proof reading, summarizing, conventional thinking) and those with similar attributes - the other dyslexics.

And make allies - you may need them for your upward or sideways moves.

6.6.9 Leave the Job Well

> **Leave the job well**
>
> 1. If it's not working, try to fix it
> 2. It it's not fixable, it's a step toward a better job
> 3. Consider moving sideways
>   - More congenial people
>   - Better suited to talents
>   - Valuable further experience
> 4. Consider moving on
>   - Leave with integrity
>   - Impress your boss on leaving
>   - Try to build up further strengths and contacts while in the job
>   - Do your homework!

So do the job well, and leave the job well.

It would be hopelessly unrealistic to pretend that all jobs - or all bosses - are well-suited to dyslexic adults. In the next section I talk about trying to craft your job to suit your strengths and passions.

But sometimes it makes more sense to move on. Many successful dyslexic people sample a range of jobs - gaining a wider range of experience and contacts - before they find the one that really suits them.

The key is to change job with style and progress, and to learn from any mistakes that you made!

First, if it is not working, try to fix it. If it is not fixable, it is a step toward a better job.

Consider moving sideways: more congenial people perhaps, better suited to talents perhaps, valuable further experience.

Consider moving on: leave with integrity, impress your boss on leaving, and try to build up further strengths and contacts as you go.

6.7 Crafting the Job

> **Crafting the Job**

I have now sketched out the stages of the job cycle. But most of the time, you will be in a job, trying to do it as best you can, and also with an eye to the future trying to move upwards, or sideways into a role that really suits you.

Unlike the plethora of books about management, or leadership, or interviews, there is remarkably little information out there about job crafting, so I need to go through this in a bit more detail.

6.7.1 Craft the job

Craft the job

1. How can you build an effective team?
2. How can you build an effective environment?
3. What needs changing to allow everyone to be more effective (and to flourish?)
4. What (distinctively!) do you like doing?
5. What valuable skills and experience do you want to build up?
6. Who do you want to impress, and how are they impressed?

So you are in the job, you are doing well. It is time to craft it to your strengths and goals. These are six of the key questions you need to be thinking about.

How can you build an effective team?

How can you build an effective environment? This is also about being personally effective, but this is also about including others - what could someone else contribute that you find hard? Organization, proof-reading, protection from interruption...

What needs changing to allow everyone to be more effective (and to flourish?) This question is about the whole team or office. How can you get more synergy between the people and tasks so that the whole becomes more than the sum of the parts and people can work to their strengths?

Question 4. What (distinctively!) do you like doing? This is about the future. In terms of your many responsibilities, what do you enjoy? What are you particularly good at and bad at? Your target is to keep crafting your job towards your strengths and preferences.

Question 5. What valuable skills and experience do you want to build up? This is also about the future, in terms of managing and developing your talents - keeping your options open so that you can continue progressing within your organization, or move on to a different one.

Question 6. Who do you want to impress, and how are they impressed? This is directly about promotion. Who is it you really need to impress and what do you need to do?

6.7.2 Team Roles

Team Roles (Mumford et al. 2008)

	Role	Description
Task	Contractor	Coordinates actions of other group
	Creator	Creative drive underlying team, novel
	Contributor	Contributes specific expertise
	Completer	Committed to getting it done
	Critic	Looks for problems
Social	Calibrator	Monitoring, conflict resolution
	Communicator	Maintaining open stream of communication
	Cooperator	Get on with the plan
Boundary	Coordinator	Also considers outside groups
	Consul	Resources, access

-> four investigations:
(i) what are your best roles
(ii) what are the best roles for each of your colleagues
(iii) what roles are not filled by allocating people to their strengths
(iv) how can the system be changed so that everyone has an effective role?

As a particular example, one that will work in both conventional and unconventional organizations, consider teamwork. This recent analysis by Troy Mumford and his colleagues gives an outstanding opportunity to get a team humming [114].

Teamwork, we have established, is a core strength in dyslexia. It is also, in my experience, a core task - badly done - in most organizations. Just think of the endless talking-shop meetings you have endured with no outcomes or actions.

So here goes. The work by Mumford and his colleagues, first has 5 task roles:

- the Contractor, who coordinates actions of the other group members;
- the Creator, who is the creative drive underlying the team, with novel contributions;
- the Contributor, who contributes specific expertise - not specifically creative;
- the Completer, who is committed to getting it done; and
- the Critic, who looks for problems.

3 C's for Social roles.

- the Calibrator, who is there for monitoring progress and making sure that conflicts get resolved quickly;
- the Communicator, maintaining an open stream of communication within the team; and
- the Cooperator, trying to make sure that everybody gets on with doing the plan.

And then there are two external team roles, going from the team to outside - the Boundary spanners.

- the Coordinator, who also considers outside groups; and
- the Consul, who is responsible for maintaining the resources and access to other key groups.

So, when you are in team meetings (or meetings more generally), use this to undertake four investigations:

- what are your best roles ?
- what are the best roles for each of your colleagues?
- what roles are not filled by allocating people to their strengths
- how can the system be changed so that everybody is able to work to their strengths and has an effective role?

These analyses are perfect for an individual with the social and cognitive strengths of dyslexia. Imagine the power of this analysis, and the likely benefits both to the team and the organization, and how well this analysis would play in some later promotion interview!

6.7.3 Job Crafting

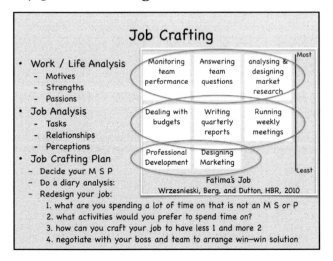

I conclude this section with some valuable ideas on job crafting provided by Amy Wrzesnieski and her colleagues [115].

The core idea behind their positive approach is work/life analysis, where you are able to identify what your motives, strengths and passions are.

And then your job analysis, which takes your tasks, and the relationships and the perceptions, and actually sees how well they match with your motives, strengths and passions.

And then creation of a job crafting plan where you decide your motives, strengths and passions, you do a diary analysis, and you redesign your job using these four criteria.

1. What are you spending a lot of time on that is not one of your motives, strengths or passions?
2. What activities would you prefer to spend time on?
3. How can you craft your job to have less 1 and more 2?
4. Negotiate with your boss and team to arrange a win-win solution.

The authors take the hypothetical case of Fatima, a middle manager. First she does a diary study (shown in the red ovals). The greater the size of the box, the more of the time spent. This diary study chart indicates that Fatima is spending most of her time on monitoring team performance, answering team questions, and directing market research.

She also spends a lot of time on preparing budgets, writing quarterly reports and running weekly meetings.

And she spends some time, but not as much as she would like, on professional development and designing marketing.

So that is the before plan. Next we try to craft the job to have more fun and more of the motives, strengths and passions.

6.7.4 Reframing Fatima's Job

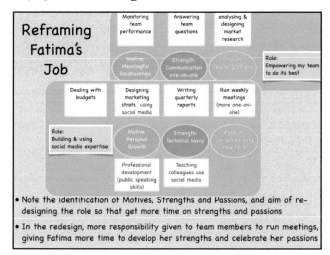

- Note the identification of Motives, Strengths and Passions, and aim of re-designing the role so that get more time on strengths and passions
- In the redesign, more responsibility given to team members to run meetings, giving Fatima more time to develop her strengths and celebrate her passions

In order to redesign her job, Fatima analyzes her motives, strengths and passions and she establishes two sets of them.

Considering the first set (at the top of the figure), the motive is for meaningful relationships. The strengths are communication one-on-one. And the passion is for teaching others.

Fatima therefore redesigns her role to be 'empowering my team to do its best in those team performance issues' - hence the entries for monitoring the team performance, and analyzing the team questions.

The second set of motives, strengths and passions, is the personal growth motive, the technical savvy strengths, and the strength for using and learning new technology. And this analysis allows her to undertake a second role, which is building and using social media expertise. And for that she is able to adapt the 'designing marketing strategies' role to 'designing strategies using social media'. And she is also able to run the weekly meetings with more of a one-to-one basis. And then she is able to design into her job professional development in terms of public speaking skills, and teaching colleagues to use social media. So that role, that second role, is building and using her social expertise.

Note the identification of Motives, Strengths and Passions and the aim of redesigning the role so that she gets more time on strengths and passions.

And in the redesign, more responsibility is given to team members to run meetings, which gives Fatima

more time to develop her strengths and celebrate her passions.

These key changes need to be negotiated with the team and with the boss, but really they should be win-win.

In my view, job crafting - both for oneself and for others - is a core skill for dyslexic people, and a central driver for 21st century success.

And whether you are dyslexic or not, job crafting is a really valuable activity to undertake.

6.8 Conclusions on Succeeding in Work

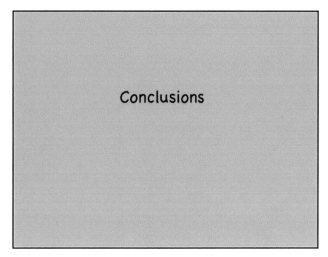

In summary, I have covered a range of topics here - career strengths, Holland Occupational Types, O*Net, Unconventional careers, building your CV, gaining and crafting your job, moving on with style.

It is time to finish!

6.8.1 Conclusions: Succeeding at Work

Conclusions: Succeeding at Work

1. Many dyslexic young adults have many of the 'Big 6' Cognitive and Social strengths. They can keep developing these strengths, and the Work Strengths during their work career.

2. Positive Dyslexia can be used to emphasize the distinctiveness of the strengths, the ability to overcome difficulties, and the continuing ability to learn on the job.

3. The Dyslexia Work Strengths Finder is a useful tool providing a profile of skills and preferences and linking to the O*Net career resource

4. Dyslexic adults can build on their strengths and weaknesses to win suitable appointments. Many career-related Positive Psychology resources are directly relevant to dyslexia, with the idea of job crafting being exceptionally valuable

5. My conclusions are very positive. With careful planning, there really is a potential 'Dyslexic Advantage' for careers, at interview stage and after.

These are my conclusions for succeeding at work.

Many dyslexic young adults have many of the 'Big 6' Cognitive and Social strengths. They can keep developing these strengths, and the Work Strengths during their work career.

Positive Dyslexia can be used to emphasize the distinctiveness of the strengths, the ability to overcome difficulties, and the continuing ability to learn on the job.

The Dyslexia Work Strengths Finder is a useful tool providing a profile of skills and preferences and linking to the O*Net careers resource.

Dyslexic adults can build on their strengths and weaknesses to win suitable appointments. Many career-related Positive Psychology resources are directly relevant to dyslexia, with the idea of job crafting being exceptionally valuable.

My conclusions are very positive. With careful planning, there really is a potential 'Dyslexic Advantage' for careers, at interview stage and afterwards.

6.9 End of Chapter 6

End of Chapter 6

That is worth repeating - "My conclusions are very positive. With careful planning, there really is a potential 'Dyslexic Advantage' for careers, at interview stage and afterwards."

Nonetheless, we must remain realistic. If the organizational culture is intrinsically anti-dyslexia, you will struggle in vain to be valued for your true worth. Moving on is generally the answer in the short-term, but the real need is to change the organizational culture.

And the key remaining issue, therefore, is how to change organizational cultures - to make them dyslexia-friendly, such that the bosses realize the advantage of having dyslexic workers. And I address this issue in the final chapter.

Chapter 7: Succeeding in Society

7.1 Chapter Introduction

Positive Dyslexia

Chapter 7:
Succeeding in Society

In Chapter 1 I presented the logic behind Positive Dyslexia, the need to work to strengths rather than weaknesses. In Chapters 2 and 3 I considered the strengths of dyslexia - what they are and why they are, ending up with the concept of delayed neural commitment. In Chapter 4 I looked at the down side - why dyslexic children often fail to thrive. In Chapters 5 and 6 I looked at Succeeding in School and then Succeeding in Work.

This is Chapter 7, Succeeding in Society. And in this capstone chapter, I take up the theme on which I ended Chapter 6 - the present organizational culture sees dyslexia as a disability, and often has an inflexible approach to job crafting. In this chapter 'Succeeding in Society' I come up with a startling answer to this problem.

7.1.1 The Positive Dyslexia Journey

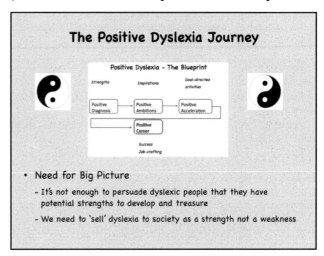

Here again is the Positive Dyslexia Journey.

The first stage was to have a Positive Assessment, based on strengths as well as weaknesses.

Then we needed to allow each individual to identify their own strengths, accelerate their development using these strengths, secure a job that suited the strengths, and go on to have a positive and rewarding life and career.

But how plausible is this!? At the end of the previous chapter I sounded a cautionary note. And here, I think, we need to see the bigger picture. It is not enough to persuade dyslexic people that they have potential strengths to develop and treasure, we need to 'sell' dyslexia to society as a strength and not a weakness.

7.1.2 Plan of Chapter

```
                Plan of Chapter

  1. Influencing People – the SPIN-Selling approach
  2. Situation for 21ˢᵗ Century CEOs
  3. Problems for 21ˢᵗ Century CEOs
  4. Implications
  5. Needs
  6. Solution
      • Talent Diversity
      • Link to Dyslexia
  7. Conclusions
```

All the other chapters have seen the problems through the eyes of a dyslexic individual, and I have done my best to reveal what the potential strengths are and how they can be identified, developed and utilized for a successful career. The idea behind this chapter is that we need to change perspective, and see the issues from the perspective of the rest of society, the opinion makers and progress drivers.

So we need to influence the important people, we need to 'sell' to them the advantages of dyslexia. I take as the driving theme Neil Rackham's concept of 'SPIN selling' which has changed the face of Sales. SPIN Selling goes through four stages - Situation, Problem, Implications, Needs (and ends up with a solution) [116].

I am thinking big here. The Situation I am considering is 'merely' the problem of Western industrial competitiveness in the 21st century.

The Solution I come up with is to recognize the importance of Talent Diversity - unconventional skills as well as conventional ones, and in doing so recognize the potential of dyslexic employees.

7.1.3 My 2020 Visions

```
              My 2020 Visions

  • Dyslexia in the Workplace
     - We cannot compete with [Google / BBC / Virgin etc]
     because they have more dyslexics than us in top positions
     - opportunity not obligation for the bosses
  • Parent
     - I know that, if we all work at it, little Johnny (or
     Jenny) has every chance of a successful and fulfilling
     career and life
     - individual planning and empowerment

  We now have the tools and the science to do this
```

Let me remind you of the aspirations for Positive Psychology that I introduced so long ago at the end of Chapter 1. And this is where I hope we will be in a few years.

First, dyslexic adults will be highly motivated to declare their dyslexia, because their organizations will value dyslexic workers for their originality of thinking, or other special skills, and will enlist them to dyslexia-friendly talent management programs.

The bosses will say, "we cannot compete with Google, BBC, Virgin etc, because they have more dyslexics than us in top positions." Dyslexia has to been seen as an opportunity, not an obligation for the bosses.

Second, parents of dyslexic children will have not only the positive schools for their child, but also a rich community of dyslexia-friendly apps and dyslexic individuals who can really accelerate their learning and progression into careers that suit their own individual strengths.

And we do now have the tools and the science to do this.

7.1.4 Vision or Mirage...

Vision or Mirage...

- Outside the dyslexia community, dyslexia is often perceived as an unwanted drain on resources that could be better utilized in addressing the organization's core activities, whether commercial or educational
- It is therefore necessary to 'rebrand' dyslexia so that a dyslexic person is seen by a school or company as a resource to be cherished rather than a load to be carried
- But how...

My initial exposition of my 2020 vision was greeted with friendly but incredulous laughter when I presented it at the 2012 IDA conference. I think some skepticism is warranted, but I was deadly serious.

This is the problem...

Only an incurable optimist would think that creating a vision, and providing some tools, is all that is needed for it to come to pass.

Unfortunately the world is not just 'not prepared' for positive dyslexia, it is actually contra-prepared. The unintended consequence of disability legislation is that employers perceive only the costs of dyslexia.

Indeed, outside the dyslexia community, dyslexia is often perceived as an unwanted drain on resources that could be better utilized in addressing the organization's core activities, whether commercial or educational.

It is therefore necessary to 'rebrand' dyslexia so that a dyslexic person is seen by a school or company as a resource to be cherished rather than as a load to be carried

But how can we do this?

7.2 SPIN

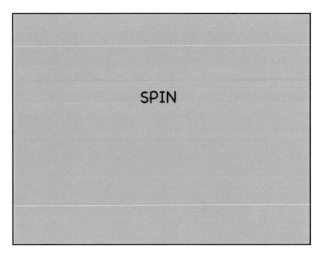

If we are to persuade society that dyslexia really does have strengths, we need to sell a vision where dyslexic people make significant contributions to society.

We therefore need to consider the most effective approaches to Sales. And the market leader in this area has for many years been Neil Rackham's revolutionary SPIN selling approach.

It is well worth going through this in some detail, because the skills of persuasion are part-and-parcel of the social skills and big picture skills that dyslexic people need to develop and utilize.

7.2.1 Strategy - SPIN

Strategy - SPIN

- Decenter from dyslexia
- Think from the stakeholders' perspective
  - Employers, co-workers
  - We're looking to 'sell' the 'dyslexia as strength' view
- SPIN approach to sales (Rackham, 1989)
  - Situation, Problem, Implications, Needs
  - Better to help with the customer's acknowledged need than to sell a solution to a problem that the customer doesn't acknowledge

I am particularly proud of my insight that we needed

to decenter from dyslexia - it is so easy to get stuck in one way of looking at a problem.

We need to consider dyslexia from the perspective of a non-dyslexic stakeholder. How can we persuade him or her that dyslexia really is a good thing, to be valued rather than tolerated? The stakeholders could be employers or could be co-workers. We are trying to 'sell' the 'dyslexia as strength' view.

The way to do this is truly to see it from their point of view.

The SPIN approach to sales (Neil Rackham's) is Situation, Problem, Implications, Needs. And the key point is that it is better to help with the customer's acknowledged need (that they have acknowledged themselves) than to sell a solution to a problem that the customer does not acknowledge.

7.2.2 SPIN Selling

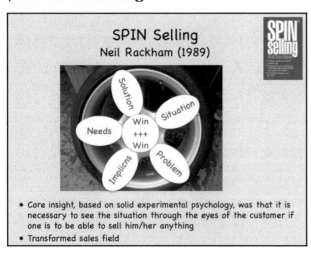

- Core insight, based on solid experimental psychology, was that it is necessary to see the situation through the eyes of the customer if one is to be able to sell him/her anything
- Transformed sales field

Here is the book 'Spin Selling' by Neil Rackham [116].

Rackham's core insight was that it is necessary to see the situation through the eyes of the customer if one is to be able to sell him/her anything.

And his approach is to go through 5 stages. First, discuss with the customer their situation, allowing them to identify the problems facing them and the implications of those problems for their business, and therefore the needs that they have for some solution. Which allows you then, to come up with a suitable solution - which is actually a win-win solution, for you and them.

And this transformed the sales field. So let us have a go at that with dyslexia.

7.3 The Situation for companies and organizations in the 21st Century

The Situation for companies and organizations in the 21st Century

We will use the SPIN methodology. No rushing straight to the hard sell. We need to go through the stages properly.

First, the people we are trying to persuade are indeed the bosses, as I argued in my original presentation. Once the bosses are persuaded, business will change, society will change, and eventually even education will change.

So what is the Situation for the bosses? The situation for companies and organizations in the 21st century.

7.3.1 21st Century Competition

21st Century competition

- "The wealth of nations, which depended upon land, labor, and capital during its agricultural and industrial phases – depended upon the natural resources, the accumulation of money, and even weaponry – will come in the future to depend upon information, knowledge and intelligence."
  - Feigenbaum, E. and McCorduck, P. (1984). The Fifth Generation: Japan's challenge to the world. Pan Books, London., p27

- "Globalisation brings opportunities and challenges. ...many of our companies have to compete with companies in emerging economies, such as China, with wage costs that can be 5 per cent of the UK's. Company strategies based on low costs alone will end up in a downward spiral, each year bringing a new low-cost competitor. ... We should seek to compete with emerging economies in a 'race to the top' rather than in a 'race to the bottom'".
  - Sainsbury Report to HM Government (2007) The Race to the Top: A Review of Government's Science and Innovation Policies

It is 30 years since Ed Feigenbaum made this observation [117]:

"The wealth of nations, which depended upon land, labor, and capital during its agricultural and industrial phases - depended upon the natural resources, the accumulation of money, and even weaponry - will come in the future to depend upon information, knowledge and intelligence."

Western governments have taken this on board, here is a quotation from the Sainsbury review from the UK government [118].

"Globalisation brings opportunities and challenges. ...many of our companies have to compete with companies in emerging economies, such as China, with wage costs that can be 5 per cent of the UK's. Company strategies based on low costs alone will end up in a downward spiral, each year bringing a new low-cost competitor. ... We should seek to compete with emerging economies in a 'race to the top' rather than in a 'race to the bottom'."

7.3.2 Competitive Advantage

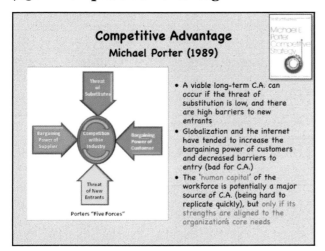

So how do we get a 'race to the top'?

The bible for most organizations from the late 20th century onwards has been Michael Porter's enduring work on competitive advantage. Almost all chief executives with strategic interests will be familiar with this Five Forces framework, which suggests that the opportunity for lasting Competitive Advantage in a market is maximized if there are low values of Competition within Industry, the Threat of Substitution, the Bargaining power of Customers, and the Bargaining power of Suppliers, but there are high barriers to new entrants.

Globalization and rapid technological change have increased the power of customers, and substantially eroded any barriers to new entrants, and so in most industries the 5 forces suggest that any current competitive advantage may be short-lived.

Arguably the greatest barrier to new entrants (and hence the greatest source of competitive advantage) is the human capital of the workforce. Skills take years to train. But the human capital is only of value if its strengths are aligned with the organization's core needs.

7.3.3 The solutions and the problems...

The solutions and the problems...

- 'Human capital' – we need more innovative, more flexible, more 'agile' workers, able to use the new technological developments to create and satisfy new markets as well as the enduring needs of leisure and service.
- Conventional education produces the logical problem solving skills and knowledge that can be replicated either by computers or by lower cost competitors.
- The 'wealth creators' – the workers who together generate 50% of the profits become more critical as organizations increase in size. For 100 it's 10 wealth creators (10%), for 1000 it's only 30 (0.3%). [Price's Law]
- Studies of expertise suggest that it takes 10 years to develop world class skills, and yet most highly talented CEOs move on within 3 years.

And so we have problems.

For 'Human capital' we need more innovative, more flexible, more 'agile' workers, able to use the new technological developments to create and satisfy new markets as well as the enduring needs of leisure and service.

Conventional education produces the logical problem solving skills and knowledge that can be replicated either by computers or by lower cost competitors.

The 'wealth creators' - the workers who together generate 50% of the profits - become more critical as organizations increase in size. For a workforce of 100 there are about 10 wealth creators (10%), for 1000 it is only about 30 (3%), which is Price's Law.

The bigger the organization the lower the proportion of wealth creators, and therefore the more critical they are.

And the most talented products of our educational

system are no longer providing the competitive advantage that used to be the case.

Studies of expertise suggest that it takes 10 years to develop world-class skills, and yet most highly talented CEOs move on within 3 years.

These are serious Problems for the bosses!

7.4 Core Personal Skills in the 21st Century: Management Blockbusters

Core Personal Skills
in the 21st Century:
Management Blockbusters

As I mentioned in Chapter 1 when describing the outstanding contributions of Positive Psychology, one of the major accomplishments was the 'Values in Action' initiative, in which Martin Seligman, Chris Peterson and their colleagues analyzed all the world's enduring religions and philosophies to establish whether they were like a series of overlapping Venn diagrams, with multiple differences but a common core. And they did identify a common core of 24 character strengths, as I reported in §1.5.5.

So I thought I would try the same approach to '21st century work skills' going through all the management blockbusters to see whether there are indeed commonalities.

The ones I will go through are the ones I happen to be familiar with. But they are pretty representative. My apologies if I have missed out one of your own favorites, but I would be very interested to have suggestions for further attributes. I think this is one of the most important undertakings we can make as a society, because it should determine the objectives

for our entire educational system. So here are 'my' management blockbusters.

7.4.1 The Learning Organization

The Learning Organization
Peter Senge (1990)

The 5 Disciplines
1. Building Shared Vision
2. (Breaking) Mental Models
3. Personal Mastery
4. Team Learning
5. Systems Thinking

I will start with Peter Senge's monumental work, entitled 'The Fifth Discipline', but basically the bible of the movement of the 'Learning Organization', an organic organization that is able to learn and adapt to the rapid societal and technological changes that Senge correctly foresaw [119].

He suggested that there are 5 disciplines

1. building shared vision;
2. critically examining habitual mental models of 'how things are';
3. personal mastery at the individual level;
4. team learning for groups of individuals;

and the key to success, the fifth discipline:

5. systems thinking which was able to see patterns of behavior over time.

Just take a moment to see how these fit with the strengths of dyslexia.

- Building shared vision - perfect, big picture approach, visualization, communication.
- Breaking habitual mental models - perfect, the dyslexic people have not formed those habits, and the creative aspect always asks 'why do we do it that way...'
- Personal mastery - usually, when dyslexic people are good, they are very very good, but there are always areas of weakness, which is why team

learning is a core strength - finding the right roles for the right people, teamwork and communication can actually help to personal mastery.

- And then finally systems thinking, Senge's major discovery, which I go through next.

7.4.2 Discipline 5: Systems Thinking

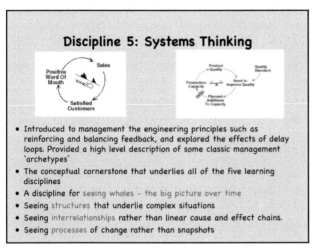

Systems thinking used the engineering principles of delay and feedback to characterize typical cyclical management situations such as the arms race, growth and underinvestment, and goal erosion.

Senge also introduced a whole range of coaching strategies based around these principles. The key ideas here are reinforcing and balancing feedback. Reinforcing feedback is shown in the figure by the snowball going down the slope getting bigger and bigger. The sales go well leading to satisfied customers, which leads to positive word-of-mouth, which leads to greater sales, which leads to more satisfied customers and so on. A vicious, but positive, cycle.

And then the other side of the coin, is the balancing feedback - which puts the brakes on. Let's say there is a need to improve quality. You have planned additions to capacity, but that slows you down and therefore that actually prevents the reinforcing feedback. And you will see also here there is the idea of delay, and delay is obviously one of the major problems in our understanding of why things go wrong.

Senge claims that systems thinking is the conceptual cornerstone that underlies all of the five learning disciplines. He also introduced a whole range of coaching strategies based around these principles.

- Systems thinking is a discipline for seeing wholes - the big picture over time. So dyslexic people have the big picture skills but the systems thinking will allow them to improve those skills substantially.

- It is a discipline for seeing structures that underlie complex situations. Seeing behind the trees to see the underlying wood.

- It highlights interrelationships rather than linear cause and effect chains.

- And it reveals processes of change rather than snapshots.

So my strong advice to any person who really enjoys personal development - is get this book and work through it - it will help you understand the levers behind everyday life, and will give you a real insight into how organizations thrive or fail, and will help you to coach others to do so.

So far so good, the Learning Organization requirements seem highly suited to dyslexic people. Let's move on.

7.4.3 The 7 habits of highly effective people

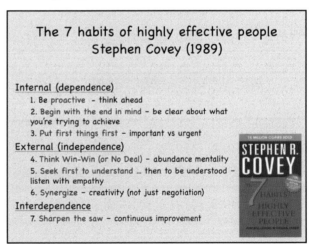

As a writer of an academic text I would be pleased if it sold 1000 copies. Covey's '7 Habits' has sold 15 million copies in 38 languages. It is a different league from academia. And it is also a very good and wise book [120].

Covey highlights the need for discipline - getting into the right habits, so one just does them. This is like the deliberate practice with expertise development, until one becomes expert in a particular skill.

So there are 7 habits. First there are three internal habits. One, be proactive - think ahead. Second, begin with the end in mind - be clear about what you are trying to achieve. And third, put first things first - distinguish between the important and the urgent, and find time to do the important things.

Three internal, then three external. So this is for dealing with other people, like the social skills. Think Win-Win (or No Deal), this is what he refers to as the abundance mentality - which is actually a bit like thinking outside the box. Seek first to understand and then to be understood - that is listen with empathy. Synergize - go for creativity where you find the creative solution, not just a negotiation.

And finally, the 7th habit is to 'sharpen the saw', that is to go for continuous improvement of your strengths. This is a reference to Abe Lincoln who was quoted as saying "If I had to chop down a tree, I would spend 90% of my time sharpening my ax." It refers to the need to hone the appropriate skills, thereby saving time in future. Basically, thinking long-term for your investments in time.

You can see again, that those seem to be pretty similar to the characteristic skills of dyslexic people.

7.4.4 Dan Pink: A whole new mind

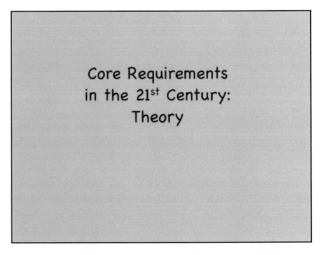

A more modern classic, that I mentioned in Chapter 6, is from best selling author and speaker Dan Pink. He makes the case that the 20th century was the age of the rational, linear, analytic problem solving skills that still provide the pinnacle of the education system.

However, Pink claims that the changes brought about by highly trained, less well paid, workers in the far east, together with the advent of computer-based replacements for middle management tasks have essentially diminished the value of these 20th century skills [108].

By contrast, the skills needed for the 21st century are the softer, synthetic, intuitive skills that are not taught at school. He describes the Six Senses (the intuitive skills):

- Design, not just function but also design;
- not just argument but also Story, that is the narrative behind it;
- not just focus but also Symphony, getting things to work together;
- not just logic but also Empathy, trying to understand where the others are thinking;
- not just seriousness but also Play, not taking everything too seriously; and
- not just accumulation of wealth, but actually searching for Meaning.

7.5 Core Requirements in the 21st Century: Theory

I now consider the core requirements of the 21st century, from the point of view of theory.

7.5.1 Strategy Maps

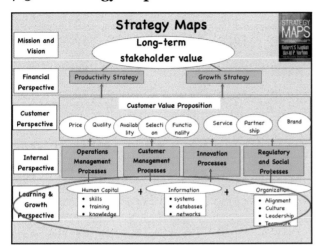

7.5.2 Shared Value

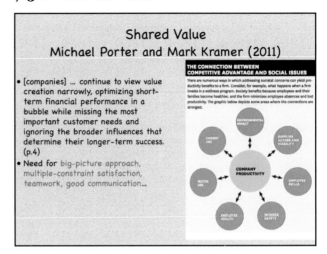

Here is the pinnacle of Strategic Planning, it is the world leading Balanced ScoreCard approach introduced by Kaplan and Norton [121].

And this is how a generic Strategy Map for an organization starts, with the Mission and Vision [122].

The Balanced ScoreCard is called Balanced because it considers four perspectives (not just the Financial), as shown on the left hand side of the figure.

- The Financial perspective;
- the Customer Perspective;
- the Internal perspective; and
- the Learning and Growth perspective.

Note that the workforce Learning and Growth perspective underpins everything else. And it includes the Human Capital of the organization as well as the information systems and the organization culture and leadership.

So even the most dedicated finance-based management theorists recognize that Human Capital is the foundation for organizational success.

I have mentioned Michael Porter before in terms of competitive advantage. Recently, he has adapted the rather stark 'Competitive Strategy' focus to take a broader view. He now advocates 'Shared Value', which may be seen as a win-win partnership between the company and its customers and the overall environment [123].

"Companies continue to view value creation narrowly, optimizing short-term financial performance in a bubble while missing the most important customer needs and ignoring the broader influences that determine their longer-term success."

Porter and Kramer argue that the shared value approach requires understanding of the Big Picture, the ability to solve wicked problems involving multiple constraints, teamwork and good communication. Again, these seem to be dyslexia-representative skills.

7.5.3 Leadership in an age of uncertainty

7.5.4 Talent Management

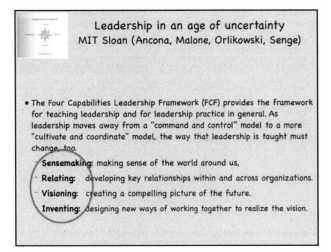

That was shared value. We have looked at the management gurus at Harvard. How about MIT!?

Here is the MIT Sloan School of Management, where they have developed the Four Capabilities Leadership Framework, which aims more at the development of human capital, and in particular the communication skills.

The Four Capabilities Leadership Framework provides the framework for teaching leadership and for leadership practice in general. The framework argues that as organizations move away from a 'command and control' model to a more 'cultivate and coordinate' model, the way that leadership is taught must also change [124].

The Framework brings out the four capabilities skills:

- Sense making: making sense of the world around us;
- Relating: developing key relationships within and across organizations;
- Visioning: creating a compelling picture of the future; and
- Inventing: designing new ways of working together to realize the vision.

It is really hard to see anything that is actually closer to the skills of dyslexic people.

Finally, Talent Management. Here is a definition from the Talent Management Handbook:

"an organizational talent management strategy comprises:

- activities and processes that involve the systematic identification of key positions which differentially contribute to the organization's sustainable competitive advantage;
- the development of a talent pool of high potential and high performing incumbents to fill these roles; and
- the development of a differentiated human resource architecture to facilitate filling these positions with competent incumbents and to ensure their continued commitment to the organization."

Putting it simply, therefore, a talent management strategy is the development of a talent pool of high potential, high performing individuals whose talent can be further developed and utilized through the talent management program.

I mentioned earlier Price's Law - that 50% of the creative work in a company would be achieved by just 30 people (in a 1000 person company). Bill Gates has an even more extreme view of the rarity and so the preciousness of these 'wealth creators', as we see in this quote here:

"Take our 20 best performers away from us and I can assure you that Microsoft would be a pretty unimportant company."

So talent is crucial to 21st century success.

7.6 What are the 'Hard-to-Develop' Skills that can give competitive advantage?

What are the 'Hard-to-Develop' Skills that can give competitive advantage?

Finally, I mentioned earlier the '10 year rule' for world-class skill - that it takes 10 years to get fully up to speed.

What are the hard-to-develop work skills that may take equally long to develop?

7.6.1 Hard-to-replicate Leadership Competences

Hard-to-replicate Leadership Competences
(Ruyle & Orr, 2011)

Leadership Competence	Developmental Difficulty	Dyslexic Strength?
Innovation management	Hardest	
Conflict management	Hardest	*
Political savvy	Hardest	*
Understanding others	Hardest	**
Negotiating	Hard	**
Sizing up people	Hard	**
Interpersonal savvy	Hard	**
Building effective teams	Hard	**
Dealing with ambiguity	Hard	**
Strategic agility	Hard	
Managing through systems	Hard	
Organizational agility	Hard	

This is an analysis by Ruyle and Orr in the Talent Management Handbook, and this led to the above findings [125].

Many skills are hard to replicate and train, but the hardest are these:

- Innovation Management;
- Conflict Management;
- Political savvy;
- Understanding others.

And then: Negotiating; Sizing up people; Interpersonal Savvy; Building effective teams; Dealing with ambiguity; Strategic agility; Managing through systems; and Organizational agility.

Those are the skills that take the longest to develop and are the hardest to develop.

But look at those: Conflict Management; Political savvy; Understanding others; Negotiating - these are classic dyslexia skills.

And indeed if you look at how they compare with our existing analysis of strengths - on the right hand side of the figure - it is clear that most of those skills are directly in synergy with our previous analogies.

7.7 The Problems for companies and organizations in the 21st Century

The Problems
for companies and organizations in the 21st Century

You have probably forgotten that I am undertaking Rackham's SPIN analysis. The previous section was the Situation for 21st century companies.

We must now move on to the P - the Problems.

I am making these quotes unattributably, but they really are characteristic of conversations I have had.

I am giving quotes from the CEOs of four very different companies, a City Council (where the workforce tend to reliable but uncreative), a small research firm (where the difficulty is hanging on to key staff), a startup (where the workforce tend to be brilliant but undisciplined), a University (where the academic staff are brilliant intellectually but varied in terms of discipline, and the students tend to be rather uncreative). And finally, a non-dyslexic employee.

7.7.1 The Chief Executive of a City Council

The Chief Executive of a City Council

- Every year we're being asked to do more and more with less and less.
- My workforce is demoralized, they're just keeping their heads down and following the rules
- We've struggled to innovate at the best of times, but at the moment morale is rock bottom, efficiency is rock bottom and innovation is non-existent.
- Our systems were designed 20 years ago, when the local government requirements were very different, and the cuts and uncertainty that we have suffered recently have been real killers

---

I start with the Chief Executive of a City Council. Here are some unattributed quotes.

"Every year we are being asked to do more and more with less and less.

My workforce is demoralized, they are just keeping their heads down and following the rules.

We have struggled to innovate at the best of times, but at the moment morale is rock bottom, efficiency is rock bottom and innovation is non-existent.

Our systems were designed 20 years ago, when the local government requirements were very different, and the cuts and uncertainty that we have suffered recently have been killers."

7.7.2 The Director of a small research firm

The director of a small research firm

- We've got some really good products, ideas and staff
- But the problem is hanging on to the good staff. They all know that their skills are in high demand, and with Rolls Royce now having a unit on the Innovation Park, they all know that they can get a very good wage and good prospects by leaving
- The problem is how to keep them happy, and how to get a balance between creativity and productivity

---

The director of a small research firm.

"We have some really good products, ideas and staff.

But the problem is hanging on to the good staff. They all know that their skills are in high demand, and with Rolls Royce now having a unit on the Innovation Park, they all know that they can get a very good wage and good prospects by leaving.

The problem is how to keep them happy, and how to get a balance between creativity and productivity."

7.7.3 The Founder of a Startup

The founder of a Startup

- It was great to get my ideas to the marketplace, and now we've got a full order book
- But all my employees are creative types, we don't seem to have anyone who can just get on and do a job properly
- I tried employing a manager, but he couldn't get his head round the way we work
- I can't keep checking everything myself, I'll have a nervous breakdown

---

The founder of a Startup.

"It was great to get my ideas to the marketplace, and now we have a full order book.

But all my employees are creative types, we don't seem to have anyone who can just get on and do a job properly.

I tried employing a manager, but he couldn't get his head round the way we work.

I can't keep checking everything myself, I'll have a nervous breakdown."

7.7.4 Vice Chancellor of a University

> ## Vice Chancellor of a University
>
> - Our mission is to provide the environment in which students can learn the knowledge and skills needed to thrive in the 21st century
> - But our students come to University from school with a 'teach me' attitude that needs to be changed before they become truly independent learners, and the knowledge we teach in any case has limited shelf life
> - The employers want them to have 'employability skills', but no-one seems to be able to say quite what these are, or how we can get them across
> - We're in a very competitive marketplace, but our job is actually to educate the 'customers' so they change their views on what a good education entails!

The Vice Chancellor of a University.

"Our mission is to provide the environment in which students can learn the knowledge and skills needed to thrive in the 21st century.

But our students come to University from school with a 'teach me' attitude that needs to be changed before they become truly independent learners, and the knowledge we teach in any case has limited shelf life.

The employers want them to have 'employability skills', but no-one seems to be able to say quite what these are, or how we can get them across.

We are in a very competitive marketplace, but our job is actually to educate the 'customers' so they change their views on what a good education entails!"

7.7.5 Non-dyslexic employee in a firm

> ## Non-dyslexic employee in a firm
>
> - We're struggling to keep our heads above water.
> - The management are talking of laying off 20% of the workforce, and yet we must give dyslexic workers extra support under the Discrimination Act.
> - It doesn't seem right, or fair to the non-dyslexic workers to use our non-existent resources this way
> - As far as I'm concerned, every worker has to be worthy of his or her pay. We can't afford to 'carry' anyone.

And finally, the non-dyslexic employee in a firm.

"We are struggling to keep our heads above water. The management are talking of laying off 20% of the workforce, and yet we must give dyslexic workers extra support under the Discrimination Act. It doesn't seem right, or fair to the non-dyslexic workers to use our non-existent resources this way.

As far as I'm concerned, every worker has to be worthy of his or her pay. We can't afford to 'carry' anyone."

7.8 The Implications for companies and organizations in the 21st Century

> The Implications
> for companies and organizations in
> the 21st Century

Those are the Problems for five different companies

and individuals. What are the Implications, then, for those companies and individuals?

7.8.1 Implications for the City Council CEO

Implications for City Council CEO

- Short term changes
  - loss of resource & staff
  - focus on KPIs
  - system streamlining
- Immediate losses
  - experience
  - creativity
  - higher stress, lower morale
  - non-essential developments

- Longer term dangers
  - process commitment
  - deskilling
  - loss of ambition
  - loss of oversight
  - loss of 'change creators'
  - mediocrity
  - loss of fitness for purpose
  - inability to change with the times

In considering the implications of these problems, I will focus on the first case, the City Council CEO, responsible for the effective provision of the civic services. I cannot spend long on this. I have neither the space nor the qualifications, but I think this analysis will strike a chord.

In the first place, following a budget cut there will have to be changes. The major cost is in fact staff salaries, and so there will have to be staff cuts. Senior staff have higher salaries, and those without clear portolios will be most at risk. The resource cuts generally mean it is necessary to focus on the core services - the Key Performance Indicators used for national reporting of performance. This will lead to streamlining of the systems to highlight performance against these targets and indeed to re-allocate resources to directly target KPI achievement

These changes will have an immediate effect - there will be a loss of experience, staff who have served range of roles in the organization and have a broader view; there will be a loss of creativity, owing to the greater emphasis on KPIs, remaining staff will be more anxious and stressed, recognizing the loss of job security, and there may be a climate of fear, with everyone keeping their head down and focusing narrowly on their own job. Non-essential developments will be sidelined.

The effects of these changes will snowball over time. Long term dangers will include 'process

commitment', that is, processes will become automatized, enshrined, fixed. There will be a continual deskilling of the workforce, with the more creative and ambitious personnel leaving, there will be a loss of 'big picture' oversight, with the organization differentiating into a series of independent 'silos' around each KPI. As the processes get more entrenched the scope for innovation diminishes, potential 'change creators' are sidelined with other tasks - or leave. In terms of human capital, the organization is left with a relatively uniform, mediocre, collection of system-followers. The organization will lose the capacity to adapt with the times, and will essentially no longer be fit for purpose.

7.8.2 The Whirlpool of Decline

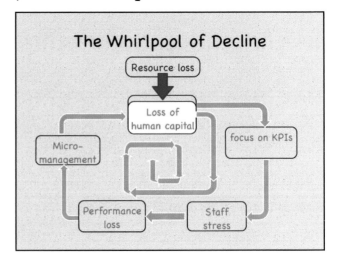

The Whirlpool of Decline

The previous figure provides the basis for a 'systems analysis' based on Senge's 'Learning Organization' framework. I call it the 'Whirlpool of decline' to highlight the cyclical nature with gradually diminishing performance over each cycle.

We start with resource loss. This leads to loss of human capital, then over-focus on a limited set of KPIs, staff stress, performance loss owing to the stress (and indeed my analyses of the effects of stress on performance that I presented in Chapter 4 are equally relevant here). This leads to performance loss. Management is under pressure to achieve the KPIs, and therefore introduces an even more micro-managed approach. Staff no longer enjoy working in the organization, and feel their skills and experience are not valued. The higher achievers take the opportunity to jump ship...

And then the cycle continues, faster and faster in ever decreasing and deepening circles.

A race to the bottom.

7.8.3 Getting the right balance of talents

> **Getting the right balance of talents ...**
>
> - Conventional organizations
>   - are struggling with rigid processes, too many conventional thinkers and too few innovative personnel
>   - the effect of competitive pressure is to exacerbate the problem
>   - There doesn't seem to be any easy way to train up conventional thinkers to become skilled in the non-conventional, intuitive skills
> - Small creative companies
>   - are struggling with too many creative thinkers and too few conventional thinkers
>   - the effect of competitive pressure is to exacerbate the problem
>   - There doesn't seem to be any easy way to train up non-conventional thinkers to become skilled in the conventional, problem-solving skills and communication is difficult

The need to attain and nurture the right balance of talents is therefore at the heart of the Implications of the problems for conventional companies.

For conventional organizations, they are struggling with rigid processes, too many conventional thinkers and too few innovative personnel. The effect of competitive pressure is to exacerbate the problem. There is no easy way to train up conventional thinkers to become skilled in the non-conventional, intuitive skills.

An equivalent talent balance problem arises for small creative companies, though this time it is the other way round. They are struggling with too many creative thinkers and too few conventional thinkers. The effect of competitive pressure is to exacerbate the problem. And there is no easy way to train up non-conventional thinkers to become skilled in the conventional problem-solving skills, and communication between the two groups of people is difficult.

So that is a quick overview of the Implications, I will return to these and the other cases following my proposed solutions.

7.9   The Needs for 21st Century Companies

> **The Needs
> for 21st Century Companies:**

We now move on to the Needs and the Solutions. First, the Needs for 21st Century Companies.

7.9.1 21st Century Strengths

> **21st Century Strengths**
>
> 1. The Knowledge Economy
> 2. Avoiding 'competition to the bottom'
> 3. Popular concepts
>   - Human Capital
>   - Competitive Advantage
>   - 8 Hard-to-train competences - Ruyle & Orr 2007
>   - Four Capabilities Framework – MIT Sloan
>   - Seven Habits - Stephen Covey
>   - The 6 senses - Dan Pink – Whole New Mind
>   - The 5 dimensions - Peter Senge – the learning organization

I have presented a pretty wide range of highly respected and influential published work on what these hard-to-replicate 21st century skills might be.

It is now time to do what the Positive Psychology group did for the world's religions and try to create the Venn diagrams between them all to see whether there is any common core.

Here are all the sources I have referenced in this chapter, covering both popular and academic approaches to management.

- First, the Knowledge Economy.

- Second, avoiding 'competition to the bottom'.

- Third, popular concepts: Human Capital; Competitive Advantage; 8 Hard-to-train competences; Four Capabilities Framework; Seven Habits; The 6 senses; The 5 dimensions.

Let's put them all on the same diagram.

7.9.2 21st Century Strengths

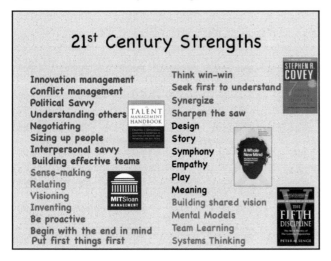

Here goes: The 8 Special skills: Innovation management; Conflict management; Political Savvy; Understanding others; Negotiating; Sizing up people; Interpersonal savvy; Building effective teams.

The Four Capabilities: Sense-making; Relating; Visioning; Inventing.

The 7 habits. The 6 senses. And 4 of the 5 disciplines.

7.9.3 21st Century Strengths: Work Strengths, Mental Strengths, Social Strengths

21st Century Strengths		
Work Strengths	**Mental Strengths**	**Social Strengths**
Be proactive	Synergize	Think win-win
Sharpen the saw	Inventing	Seek first to understand
	Sense-making	Relating
	Design	Conflict management
		Political Savvy
	Visioning	Understanding others
	Story	Negotiating
	Symphony	Sizing up people
	Mental Models	Interpersonal savvy
	Put first things first	Building effective teams
	Begin with the end	Team Learning
	in mind	Building shared vision
	Meaning	
Play	Innovation management	Empathy
	Systems Thinking	

Can we make any sense out of these? Let's put them into the three categories, the Work Strengths, the Mental Strengths, and the Social Strengths.

As shown in the figure, that's pretty good. We have placed everything except Play.

You can see there is a lot of Mental Strengths, a lot of Social Strengths.

Just two Work Strengths, I guess that's because the Work Strengths are conventionally seen as 20th century strengths as opposed to 21st century strengths.

So how do these correspond to the strengths triads that we found characterized Dyslexia?

7.9.4 21ˢᵗ Century Strengths: Strengths Triads

Well, that is extraordinary!

We have found 7 of the 9 characteristic skills of dyslexia!

For the work skills triad we have Proactivity, though Determination / Resilience isn't there, and neither is Flexible Coping.

But all three mental strengths are strongly represented - Innovation, Big Picture, Visuo-Spatial.

As are the Social Skills Triad - Teamwork, Empathy. Communication

Isn't this amazing!? I swear that Sara and I did the dyslexia skills analysis two years before I did this analysis of 21st century skills.

So, there is a terrific match between the 21st century strengths as indicated by the recent theorists who have nothing to do with dyslexia, and the dyslexia decathlon which we developed earlier.

7.10 The Solution for 21ˢᵗ Century Companies: Talent Diversity

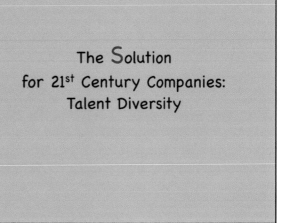

So those are the needs. We're still doing SPIN. Now it is time for the Solution I should be able to 'sell' to the CEOs and the workforce of those four types of company I interviewed...

The Solution I propose is what I call Talent Diversity - having a range of talents within the organization, and having working methods designed such that people of different talents are able to work to their strengths.

This is not directly related to dyslexia at all.

7.10.1 A Bird's Eye View of Diversity Progress

A Bird's Eye View of Diversity Progress
Butler (2011) p.404

- Recruitment programs designed to meet legal obligations have become recruitment and retention programs that reflect how demographic trends will impact the labor market in the future
- What began as an effort to hire and promote minorities has led to a culture of inclusion that not only allows but indeed encourages all employees to contribute in different ways
- Commitment to fairness and equality has become an understanding that cognitively diverse organizations often outperform those that draw on homogeneous talent bases
- While diversity was once the exclusive domain of the human resources department, today it is the personal responsibility of everyone – corporate leaders and all employees companywide.

Let me set the scene by providing independent evidence that diversity is not just an obligation but actually is now accepted as a genuine benefit to an organization.

Again taken from the Talent Management Handbook - the only mention of talent diversity I could find in the whole handbook. And this is Butler's chapter [126].

"Recruitment programs designed to meet legal obligations have become recruitment and retention programs that reflect how demographic trends will impact the labor market in the future.

What began as an effort to hire and promote minorities has led to a culture of inclusion that not only allows but indeed encourages all employees to contribute in different ways.

Commitment to fairness and equality has become an understanding that cognitively diverse organizations often outperform those that draw on homogeneous talent bases.

While diversity was once the exclusive domain of the human resources department, today it is the personal responsibility of everyone - corporate leaders and all employees companywide."

So that is typically ethnic diversity, and gender diversity, and possibly age diversity. But the principle is exactly the same for talent diversity.

7.10.2 Talent Diversity

Talent Diversity

- Most organizations focus - for recruitment and promotion - on the 20th century talents of analysis, rational thinking, planning, target completion. But what about the important unconventional talents?
- For any organization it is necessary to have a range of talents - talent diversity - since otherwise there is a danger of groupthink and stagnation.
- Diversity in terms of gender, culture and age are already well established as beneficial both for equity and for effectiveness
- It is an extraordinary oversight that talent diversity has not had an equivalent drive to implement
- What we need is a comprehensive system to 'design in', identify and accelerate talent diversity.

So here is my Talent Diversity proposal.

Most organizations focus - for recruitment and promotion - on the 20th century talents of analysis, rational thinking, planning, target completion. But what about the important unconventional talents?

For any organization it is necessary to have a range of talents - talent diversity - since otherwise there is a danger of groupthink and stagnation.

Diversity in terms of gender, culture and age is already well established as beneficial both for equity and for effectiveness.

It is an extraordinary oversight that talent diversity has not had an equivalent drive to implement.

What we need is a comprehensive system to 'design in', identify and accelerate talent diversity.

7.10.3 The SPIN Offer to the CEO

The SPIN Offer to the CEO

- So your Situation is that you have an excellent, well-run organization, but you are concerned that competition from the far east is making it non-competitive
- The Problem is that the competition can reduce costs quicker than you can, laying off people has a range of unintended consequences, and future strategy is therefore unclear
- The Implications are pretty dire
- What you really Need is to recruit new people with the right blend of 21st Century skills, so that your teams work more effectively.
- What would you say if I told you that recruiting an extra 5% to your workforce, who have the skills you need, could double your productivity and give you a lasting competitive advantage?
- What would you say if I told you that you already have these people working for you, and all you need to do is get them onto your talent management program so they can further refine the necessary skills?

I think you will find this proposal pretty compelling. This is our SPIN Offer to the CEO.

"So your Situation is that you have an excellent, well-run organization, but you are concerned that competition from the far east is making it non-competitive.

The Problem is that the competition can reduce costs quicker than you can, laying off people has a range of unintended consequences, and future strategy is therefore unclear.

The Implications are pretty dire.

What you really Need is to recruit new people with the right blend of 21st Century skills, so that your teams work more effectively.

What would you say if I told you that recruiting an extra 5% to your workforce, who have the skills you need, could double your productivity and give you a lasting competitive advantage?

What would you say if I told you that you already have these people working for you, and all you need to do is get them onto your talent management program so they can further refine the necessary skills?"

I think, as I say, the CEO's would be very interested in this proposal.

7.11 Moving Forward: Talent Diversity

> ### Moving Forward:
> ### Talent Diversity

We have made some extraordinary progress. I started the chapter by saying we needed to decenter from dyslexia, and we should actually look at things from the perspective of the bosses of companies and organizations.

I adopted Neil Rackham's SPIN Selling framework, first establishing that the Situation was difficult for most companies, and the key problem was to balance 21st century skills with 20th century skills.

The Implications of difficulties in getting 'wealth creators' with 21st century skills were grave, but these skills cannot quickly be trained.

The Need therefore was to find a source of people with 21st century skills.

My digression on what are the 21st century skills revealed a remarkable convergence between these skills and those we had earlier established as

characteristic of dyslexia. Of course many non-dyslexic people will also have these skills, but the key point here is that every organization has an untapped (and unsuspecting) source of 21st century skills - its dyslexic workers!

So, how do we move forward from here - the key is to 'embed' the idea of Talent Diversity throughout organizational cultures.

7.11.1 The Talent Diversity Index

> ## The Talent Diversity Index
>
> - The concept of a Talent Diversity Index is a powerful one. It will become one of the KPIs for the HR Department. The TDI reflects the proportions of conventional and unconventional talents within the organization
> - The key idea is that there should be a balance of each type for each organization
> - Note that unconventional, creative companies are likely to have a high proportion of unconventional talents and a low proportion of conventional talents, whereas the opposite occurs for a conventional organization
> - This means, paradoxically, that the greatest need for unconventional thinkers (and hence the best job prospects with an appropriate Talent Management System) for unconventional thinkers is in conventional organizations!

Oversimplifying considerably, I will distinguish just two types of talent - conventional and unconventional - but the unconventional talent actually is short-hand for the variety of work skills, mental skills and social skills I derived earlier.

For any organization it is important to have a balance of diverse talents. For a creative organization that balance might be roughly 50:50, whereas for a conventional organization it might be 90% conventional, 10% unconventional.

Here I introduce the idea of a Talent Diversity Index, and I think this is a powerful one. It will become one of the key performance indicators for the HR Department. The TDI reflects the proportions of conventional and unconventional talents within the organization - and if if an organization is out of balance with the benchmark for its own industry, then it needs to change one way or the other.

So the key idea is that there should be a balance.

Unconventional, creative companies are likely to need a relatively high proportion of unconventional talents and a low proportion of conventional talents, whereas the opposite occurs for a conventional organization.

This means, paradoxically, that the greatest need for unconventional thinkers (and hence their best job prospects given an appropriate Talent Management System) is actually in a conventional organization, because conventional organizations do not normally attract unconventional talents. This is fortunate because the conventional organizations employ many more people!

7.11.2 Design for Talent Diversity

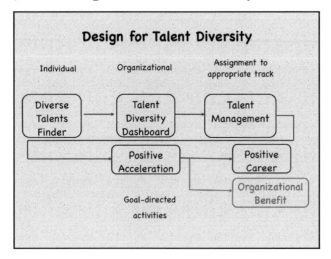

So here is a Design for Talent Diversity.

I provided extensive evidence that people with the unconventional skills associated with (but not restricted to) dyslexia can have an important role as wealth creators within an organization.

And here is my suggestion for the Design - it is similar to the Positive Dyslexia Blueprint. We create a Diverse Talents Finder, which is similar in many ways to the DWSF, but is not directly related to dyslexia.

The Diverse Talents Finder leads to a classification of each individual in terms of their skills and preferred activities. These can then be collated for the organization as a whole, leading to a Talent Diversity Index and a 'Talent Diversity Dashboard' of the tapestry of human capital talents in the organization - in much the same way as current diversity dashboards monitor gender diversity, ethnic diversity and age diversity. If there is an imbalance compared with the target balance, then recruitment should be

suitably adjusted towards the under-represented talent.

The outcome is therefore a win-win solution, where people with appropriate talents get allocated to an appropriate Talent Management System.

And then they get positively accelerated, with goal-directed activities for those talents, and maybe communicating with the others. That then leads to a positive career. This is pretty similar so far to the Positive Dyslexia blueprint.

But the key advantage and the key purpose of this chapter, is that it also leads directly to organizational benefits. We have therefore achieved the goal of providing an incentive for the bosses to value and develop individuals with unconventional skills (including dyslexic individuals, but also including non-dyslexic individuals with the appropriate skills).

We have therefore achieved benefit for the organization, benefit for the dyslexic individuals, and benefit for non-dyslexic individuals who show non-conventional strengths.

7.11.3 Talent Diversity at Work

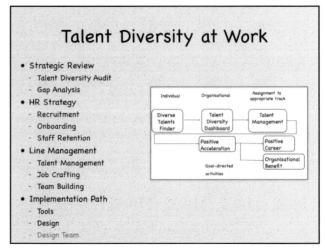

I am returning to the Problems of those chief executives that I mentioned to you before. Has the Talent Diversity framework provide them with a Solution!?

I will start with Talent Diversity at Work - this is how the Talent Diversity approach might work in practice.

First we have a Strategic Review, so we get the Talent

Diversity Audit, we do Gap Analysis - how close are we to where we wish to be.

Then that leads into the HR Strategy of Recruitment of the appropriate people. When the appropriate people are recruited they are 'onboarded', that is they are welcomed into the organization and trained. This leads to greater Staff Retention.

In terms of Line Management we have Talent Management, Job Crafting and Team Building. And in terms of the Implementation Path, we have the Tools and the Design, and the Design Team.

And a key point here is that the Design Team should surely include individuals showing a range of talents, and in particular at least one with non-conventional strengths. As I noted in Chapter 6, using the Mumford teamwork model, there are at least 10 roles within a team, and several are particularly suited to individuals with non-convention skills.

So that is Talent Diversity at Work.

7.11.4 Talent Diversity at University

How about Talent Diversity at University?

Universities are supposed to be developing the talents needed for work life. Consequently this necessitates a complete revision of University priorities. Most Universities are stuck in the 20th century (or earlier in some cases).

How does it go? A similar approach to Talent Diversity at Work. A Strategic Review: an analysis of the Key Outcome Skills, a Gap Analysis of how the current system fits that outcome analysis.

The Student Experience: Recruitment, Onboarding, Learning opportunities, Assessment methods, Talent Management and the Degree Crafting and Team Experience - all designed to help the students get those key outcome skills, which will be the 21st century skills I was talking about.

The Implementation Path: the Tools - well in fact of course we have terrific tools, now, available, including all of the new technology tools. And again the importance of team building where we actually have teams with non-conventional skills as well.

7.11.5 Talent Diversity at School

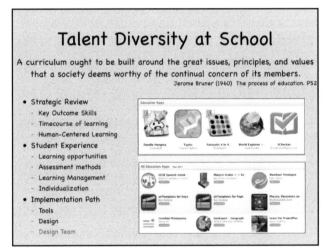

Now let me move onto Talent Diversity at School.

In my experience, school education is more resistant to change than University education. But schools are supposed to be developing the talents needed for work life, as this quotation from Jerome Bruner (many years ago) makes clear [127].

"A curriculum ought to be built around the great issues, principles, and values that a society deems worthy of the continual concern of its members."

I have suggested that the 21st century society must show concern over the talent diversity issues.

Therefore, there is a similar process: a Strategic Review: Key Outcome Skills for school education; the Timecourse of learning; and Human-Centered Learning.

The Student Experience: Learning opportunities, Assessment methods, Learning Management, Individualization.

And then the Implementation Path: the Tools - again they are in abundance with the apps and the new technology - the Design, and again the Design Team.

What we need to do is make sure we get non-conventional thinkers onto the Design Team. There are far too few in current Educational Theory and Practice.

7.12 Conclusions on Succeeding in Society

Conclusions on
Succeeding in Society

It has been a long journey, as promised, but we have reached the end of the chapter.

7.12.1 Chapter Summary

Chapter Summary

- Positive Dyslexia has the aim of helping dyslexic individuals to discover their strengths and use their strengths – at school and at work.
    - BUT a 'pressure campaign' is likely to be counter-productive.
    - It is vital to offer a solution to the problems one's key partners are suffering, rather than a solution to one's own problems!
- The key problems faced by any country, and any organization
    - how to maintain both competitive advantage and quality of life
    - how to find wealth creators with 'whole brain' skills
- Using best practice in a range of disciplines, I identified 24 skills that seem to characterize the unconventional, 'hard to develop' 21st Century skills, needed for organizations to thrive. There is a perfect match with the Dyslexia Decathlon strengths!
- The solution to the two key problems, therefore, is to manage talent diversity – both the conventional and unconventional skills.
    - Everyone can use either conventional or unconventional thinking modes, but the strengths of dyslexic individuals reflect a preference for whole brain processing, and these unconventional abilities, once lost, are hard to regain
- This has significant implications both for adult life and for education

Positive Dyslexia has the aim of helping dyslexic individuals to discover their strengths and use their strengths - at school and at work.

Unfortunately, a 'pressure campaign' is likely to be counter-productive. It is vital to offer a solution to the problems one's key partners are suffering, rather than a solution to one's own problems!

The key problems faced by any country, and any organization are how to maintain both competitive advantage and quality of life. And how to find wealth creators with 'whole brain' skills.

Using best practice in a range of disciplines, I identified 24 skills that seem to characterize the unconventional, 'hard to develop' 21st Century skills, needed for organizations to thrive. There is a near-perfect match with the Dyslexia Decathlon strengths!

The solution to the two key problems, therefore, is to manage Talent Diversity - both the conventional and unconventional skills.

Every individual has a combination of both conventional and unconventional thinking modes, but the strengths of dyslexic individuals reflect a preference for whole brain processing, and these unconventional abilities, once lost, are hard to regain.

This has significant implications both for adult life and for education.

7.13 Conclusions on Positive Dyslexia

Conclusions on
Positive Dyslexia

It has indeed been a long journey, as promised, but we have reached the end of the road...

Sometimes it has seemed like Pilgrim's Progress.

7.13.1 Pilgrim's Progress

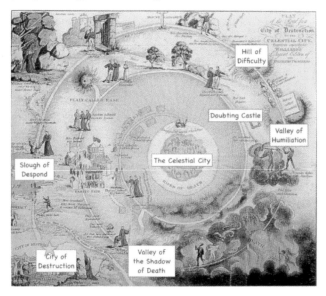

Positive Dyslexia is for all Dyslexic people, not just a few fortunate people who have privileged environments or exceptional talents.

In the journey through life for dyslexic people, we seem to be starting at the City of Destruction, going through the Slough of Despond, the Hill of Difficulty, the Valley of Humiliation, even the Valley of the Shadow of Death, Doubting Castle...

But I hope we will get in due course, by careful journey, to the Celestial City - where everything becomes clear.

If we can maintain focus on developing and using our skills, there is every chance that we will indeed be able to reach our own version of the Celestial City.

7.13.2 Summary on Positive Dyslexia

Overall Summary on Positive Dyslexia

- Positive Dyslexia accentuates the positives - 'following your star'. All it asks is that you find your 'personal best' skills and try to use them
- Most dyslexic people have difficulties in 'brain-based learning' but have compensating strengths in 'mind-based learning'
- These strengths can be characterized as arising from 'Delayed Neural Commitment' which causes short-term difficulties but holds the promise of longer-term benefits
- Many dyslexic people have - or can develop - skills in the Work Strengths Triad, the Cognitive Strengths Triad, and the Social Strengths Triad
- These 'unconventional' talents are difficult to learn conventionally, but are fully aligned with the talents needed for '21st century wealth creators'

Here at last is my overall summary on Positive Dyslexia.

Positive Dyslexia accentuates the positives - 'following your star'. All it asks is that you find your 'personal best' skills and try to use them.

Most dyslexic people have difficulties in 'brain-based learning' but can have compensating strengths in 'mind-based learning'.

These strengths can be characterized as arising from 'Delayed Neural Commitment' which causes short-term difficulties but holds the promise of longer-term benefits.

Many dyslexic people have - or can develop - skills in the Work Strengths Triad, the Cognitive Strengths Triad, and the Social Strengths Triad.

These 'unconventional' talents are difficult to learn conventionally, but are fully aligned with the talents needed for '21st century wealth creators'.

7.13.3 Conclusions on Positive Dyslexia

Conclusions on Positive Dyslexia

- Our companies, our Universities and our schools need to recognize Talent Diversity and to introduce Talent Diversity programs. These will allow all children and adults to find, develop and celebrate their talents
- Positive Dyslexia is really 'Positive Living'. It applies to all of us, dyslexic or not. We all need to develop our unique talents, and to craft careers in which we utilize them
- There is much to be done, but we have the vision, the science, the technology and the social media to transform the world

In conclusion: our companies, our Universities and our schools need to recognize Talent Diversity and to introduce Talent Diversity programs. These will allow all children and adults to find, develop and celebrate their talents.

Positive Dyslexia is really 'Positive Living'. It applies to all of us, dyslexic or not. We all need to develop our unique talents, and to craft careers in which we utilize them.

There is much to be done, but we have the vision, the science, the technology and the social media to transform the world.

7.14 End of Chapter 7 and End of the Book!

End of Chapter 7
and
End of the Book!

Positive Dyslexia will change the world for good
Its time has come
Please help!

Positive Dyslexia will change the world for good.

Its time has come.

Please help!

Glossary

Acceleration	A key concept in Positive Dyslexia, in which efforts are made to Accelerate a person's learning towards their goals and targets.
acquired learning disability	A learning disability that arises after birth, through some accident or adverse series of experiences. As opposed to a developmental learning disability, which is present from birth.
adaptation	One of the four stages I propose for helping dyslexic children learn at school.
alphabetic	A stage in learning to read, according to Frith's 1987 model, in which children learn that words are made of letters, and the letter sounds when combined lead to the sounds of the words. Frith believes this is the key stage where dyslexic children's difficulties appear. As opposed to the logographic stage.
andragogy	The scientific study of adult learning (as opposed to pedagogy, which is the scientific study of child learning).
app	A computer-based self-contained 'application', which typically may be downloaded from a central server, such as Apple's app store or Google's app stores. May well work on mobile phones or tablets via Apple ios or Google Android.
automaticity	The ability to carry out a procedure such as walking, driving, multiplying numbers with minimal need for conscious effort. More like a habit. Occurs through long practice in appropriate conditions.
automatization	The process of making skills automatic. Proposed as a specific weakness of dyslexic people, and the underpinning framework for Delayed Neural Commitment.
balancing feedback	A form of feedback in Senge's framework that tends to slow down changes in a system. As opposed to Reinforcing feedback, which amplifies change, leading to instability.
basal ganglia	Parts of the sub-cortical structures in the brain thought to be involved in automatic response selection.
Big 6	These are the Cognitive Skills Triad and the Social Skills Triad in the Dyslexia Decathlon of skills.
Big Picture	One of the Cognitive Skills Triad. The ability to see beyond the detail to the overall 'shape' of the problems or situation. To be able to see the wood rather than the trees. To get the 'helicopter view'.
brain-based learning	I use this term to refer to the 'procedural' learning capabilities of statistical learning, reinforcement learning and supervised learning. As opposed to 'mind-based' or declarative learning. I claim that dyslexic people have problems with brain-based learning, counterbalanced by strengths in declarative learning.
bricolage	A Piagetian term indicating that new learning and brain structures use the materials already developed in previous learning.
brown field learning	Learning in a context where prior learning has already taken place, and so old habits have to be (at least partially) 'unlearned' before new learning can

	be effective. As opposed to 'green field learning' where no relevant prior learning has taken place.
cerebellar deficit hypothesis	The hypothesis, proposed by Nicolson, Fawcett and Dean (1995), that the core problems in dyslexia are attributable to impaired functioning of the cerebellum and the neural circuits in which it participates.
cerebellar stimulation	Activities designed to stimulate the cerebellum - very often involving coordinative bodily movement, or doing two things at once. There is now evidence that coordinative movement training leads to neurogenesis (new cell formation) in the hippocampus and the cerebellum.
cerebellum	The 'hind brain'. A large and ancient brain structure known to be centrally involved in physical coordination and procedural learning, with a unique contribution to error-based learning.
Cognitive Skills Triad	The skills of Big Picture thinking, Visualization and Innovation. There is evidence (Chapter 2) that many dyslexic people have the opportunity to develop these skills to become distinctive strengths. Also referred to as the Mental Skills Triad. See also the Dyslexia Decathlon.
Communication	One of the Social Skills Triad, building on the ability to put oneself in the position of the listener.
confusion	The result of overloading a person's capacity for learning, and a potent barrier to learning. I claim that this is likely to lead to 'mental abscesses' in the context of that confusion.
contra-prepared	A technical term introduced by Martin Seligman to explain why people can do some things naturally, but other things are extremely hard to learn. Many of the skills in learning to read are contra-prepared.
crafting the job	Adjusting the job requirements so that one spends more time working to one's motivations, strengths, or one's passions.
declarative	Available to conscious introspection, usually language-based. I refer to this as 'mind-based'. As opposed to procedural, which uses the lower-level brain processes not accessible to consciousness. I claim that dyslexic people often have distinct strengths in declarative skills.
delayed neural commitment	The claim that dyslexic people require more time, or higher quality learning experiences, in order to build automatic skills, or new neural circuits. The term neural commitment refers to an irreversible change to the ensemble of neurons involved in a task. It derives from research on early language, but is used more generally within this book as the source both of strengths and of weaknesses for dyslexic individuals.
Determination / Resilience	One of the Work Skills Triad of the Dyslexia Decathlon. Determination is the will to keep trying. Resilience is the ability to cope with adversity. Both these are associated with success in later life.
DNA methylation	DNA is the genetic code. DNA methylation is a method 'turning off' particular genes so that they do not get expressed, thus leading to profound subsequent changes, and getting round the fact that genes are fixed from conception.
DNC	Delayed Neural Commitment
DWSF	Dyslexia Work Strengths Finder

Dynamic Reasoning	The fourth 'MIND' strength in 'The Dyslexic Advantage' book by Brock and Fernette Eide.
Dyslexia Decathlon	The 10 skills made up by the Work Strengths Triad, the Cognitive Strengths Triad and the Social Strengths Triad, capped by Unconventional Thinking. I use the word decathlon to indicate that these strengths are all skills that can be improved, and that often they reinforce each other.
Dyslexia Ecosystem	The whole system for dyslexia, including not just dyslexic people, but also their teachers, the researchers, the dyslexia organizations, and society in general. I argue that there are good solutions that apply at the level of the whole ecosystem that cannot be created if one just considers one facet in isolation.
Dyslexia Journey	The many-year progression through finding one's strengths to developing the strengths, to finding a job that suits the strengths, to crafting the job to align with the strengths.
Dyslexia Work Strengths Finder	A system intended for individuals to identify their work strengths, or for an organization to identify the strengths of its dyslexic employees so as to make the best use of the diverse talents in its workforce.
Dyslexic Advantage	An influential book by Brock and Fernette Eide, providing a rich picture of the 'MIND' Strengths of dyslexic people.
Dyslexic Automatization Deficit hypothesis	The well-established hypothesis that dyslexic people take longer to build habits, to make skills automatic.
Empathy	One of the Social Skills Triad. The ability to see things from other people's point of view.
encapsulation	Of a skill or mental process - the ability of the neural circuits involved to complete that process without needing input from any other circuits in the brain. An aspect of skill automaticity. Encapsulated processes are much more efficient but much harder to change.
Enrichment	Providing additional items in the environment to lead to better learning.
Entrepreneur	Someone showing enterprise, usually in business but also in social areas. Often considered a potential strength of dyslexic people.
epigenetic	The study of heritable changes that are not directly caused by genes - literally outside-genetic. At the cell level this often involves changes in the likelihood of a gene being expressed. It is now realized that epigenetic effects are a mechanism by which experiences can indirectly affect the effective genome.
error-dependent learning	Also known as supervised learning, the automatic capability of reducing the error in an action following error feedback. Normally needs the error-feedback circuitry of the cerebellum.
executive function	A reference to the 'central executive', the action controller at the heart of our conscious processing - maintaining goals, choosing between actions, attending to specific dimensions, coordinating activities, self control, working memory. Executive function develops strongly throughout the first 10 years of life.
Flexible Coping	One of the Work Skills Triad, the ability to think of an alternative way of proceeding when problems arise. Claimed to be a specific potential strength of dyslexia, possibly attributable to lack of habit, and frequent need to cope

	with problems.
Formal Operations	The final stage of cognitive development, according to Piaget, in which the child becomes able to think in abstract terms, coordinating several abstract dimensions at the same time. A key requirement for effective thinking. Only a minority of adults achieve formal operations.
Gene expression	The process of turning genes into (usually) proteins in the cell and thereby optimizing cell function in a given environment. Genes are expressed following all actions. The two main steps are gene transcription and then translation (into proteins). Cells can control which genes get transcribed and which transcripts get translated, providing great flexibility. Gene expression happens all the time, in response to every action and stimulus.
gene transcription	The first stage in gene expression, where DNA is changed to RNA, providing the code for translating the genetic information into proteins within the cell.
Gramma	A Dutch computer-based reading support set of programs shown to be effective in helping dyslexic children.
Graphogame	A Finnish computer-based reading support set of programs now translated into many languages and shown to be effective in helping dyslexic children.
green field	As in a green field site in building, where there is no prior building (as opposed to a brown field, pre-built) site. I arge that dyslexic children have particular difficulties with brown field learning, and therefore that it is necessary to plan the green field learning with great care.
habit	A relatively stereotyped set of actions in response to a given situation. Usually undertaken without much need for conscious monitoring. The product of long term automatization. A key claim of the automatization deficit hypothesis is that dyslexic people take longer to build up habits, and therefore have the opportunity for more flexible responding.
Human Capital	The contribution made to an organization by the strengths and talents of its workforce. A key requirement for an organization's success, just as much as financial capital.
Inoculation	A term used by Seligman to refer to activities that minimize the damage caused by subsequent adverse experiences, often associated with the building of resilience, but more generally, successful preparation for future challenges.
Interconnected Reasoning	The second 'MIND' strength in 'The Dyslexic Advantage' book by Brock and Fernette Eide.
Interpretative Phenomenological Analysis	A method of analyzing the content of interviews and the like to identify the major themes involved. A specific form of qualitative analysis.
learned helplessness	A term due to Seligman. Repeated, inescapable 'punishments' in a given situation can lead to 'giving up' so that no effort is made to cope with the difficulties.
Learning Propensity Assessment Device	Feuerstein's method for finding a person's learning propensity, their potential for moving on to the next stage of understanding in a given topic.
logographic	Reading a word as a single unit (not realizing that it is made up of letters). An early stage in learning to read in Frith's (1987) model.

Material Reasoning	The first 'MIND' strength in 'The Dyslexic Advantage' book by Brock and Fernette Eide.
mediated learning	Learning that is supported via another (more experienced) person. A central part of Feuerstein's approach. A key difference from ordinary classroom teaching is the one-to-one, learner-centered aspect.
mental abscess	A term I introduce as a metaphor to explain the catastrophic effects of repeated and hurtful failures in a given situation. Once a mental abscess is created, it is no longer possible to function effectively in that situation, and the mind-based learning capabilities are disabled.
mental lesion	A halfway house to a mental abscess - the effect of a series of mental scratches, by analogy to an open wound.
mental scratch	A single hurtful experience. A single mental scratch will heal easily, but repeated scratches may lead to a mental lesion and then to a mental abscess.
MIND strengths	The set of four strengths that Brock and Fernette Eide ascribe to successful dyslexic people in their book, The Dyslexic Advantage.
mind-based	I use this term to refer to declarative processes, which are accessible to conscious introspection. This is a key and distinctive capability of humans, and I argue that dyslexic people can have characteristic strengths in mind-based processing. These can counter-balance their known weaknesses in 'brain-based', procedural learning and processing.
Narrative Reasoning	The third 'MIND' strength in 'The Dyslexic Advantage' book by Brock and Fernette Eide.
National Reading Panel	A panel of the most influential US reading researchers who were assembled to survey the state of the art in the teaching of reading in the US and to make evidence-based recommendations. Their report is justly influential.
natural learning	The forms of learning that an organism is 'prepared for' by its inherited capabilities. For humans, I suggest that the natural learning activities are repetition, imitation and play.
neural systems	Collections of neurons throughout the brain that tend to be activated together. Usually involving activation in several different brain structures. A valuable recent approach to understanding brain function. Angela Fawcett and I argue that dyslexia is characterized by weaknesses in the language-specific procedural learning system.
neuro-constructivist approach	An influential approach in developmental cognitive neuroscience that holds that mature function emerges from more primitive capabilities by 'neuroconstruction', that is, building the necessary neural circuits and neural capabilities incrementally.
ontogenetic	Means starting from the beginning. Usually defined as the life history of an individual from the zygote to the mature adult.
ontogenetic causal chain	My analysis (with Angela Fawcett) of the developmental path of a dyslexic child from conception to age 10, with cerebellar deficit being the key underlying component.
Phonological Deficit Hypothesis	The belief that dyslexic children have difficulties in phonological representation and processing, and that this is the core difficulty in their learning to read.

Positive Dyslexia	The belief that every dyslexic individual has their own potential strengths, and the movement to allow every person to develop and live their strengths.
Positive Psychology	The belief that focusing on the positives - strengths, happiness, aspirations - is a powerful and necessary counter-balance to the traditional focus on problems and weaknesses
Preparation	Used in two ways within the book. The first way, introduced in Chapter 2, is the finding that successful dyslexic adults have a tendency to over-prepare for challenges and work events, This can endow advantages in work and life situations, and allows for flexible coping strategies to be used. The second usage derives from the analysis of the damage caused by 'mental abscesses'. A key implication of the mental abscess framework for barriers to dyslexic success is that each child should be Prepared so that they do NOT fail repeatedly on any task, and that therefore careful preparation of the necessary skills needs to be undertaken, using natural learning processes, in advance of the challenges of learning to read.
Proactivity	Planning ahead, and making appropriate preparations. One of the Work Skills Triad for dyslexia.
procedural	Literally, in terms of procedures - sequences of self-contained actions.
Procedural Learning Deficit	My theory (with Angela Fawcett) that dyslexic children have specific difficulties in procedural learning.
Reconfiguration	A method of overcoming mental abscesses by restructuring the brain circuitry to bypass or heal the abscess
reinforcement learning	Learning consequent on receiving a reward. A form of procedural learning
reinforcing feedback	A term due to Senge, indicating that the feedback to a system amplifies any changes, leading to escalating (positive or negative) consequences. As opposed to balancing feedback.
sensori-motor	Pertaining to input (the senses) and output ('motor', that is physical actions). Traditionally considered quite separate from cognitive (mental) processes but now seen as highly inter-related.
ShowBook	A form of electronic book that is designed both as a book (for declarative learning) and as a 'show me' for natural learning. This is the first use of the term!
Social Skills Triad	One of the three triads of the Dyslexia Decathlon. Comprises three strengths - Empathy, Teamwork and Communication
SPIN	A term due to Rackham, indicating the four pre-requisites for successful 'Selling' to a client: establishing the client's Situation, Problems, Implications and then Needs.
SPLD	SpLD is the technical term for dyslexia in the UK - Specific Learning Difficulties). It is also an acronym for the Specific Procedural Learning Deficit hypothesis for the cause of dyslexia.
square root rule	The procedural learning rate of dyslexic children is roughly half that of normally achieving children. This means that a dyslexic child will take much longer to learn a skill, with the deficit increasing with task difficulty. It will take twice as long for a task taking four trials to learn but 10 times as long for a task taking 100 trials.

statistical learning	A fundamental form of mammalian learning in which, over time, the brain automatically self-organizes itself to recognize the statistical regularities in the input. A form of procedural learning.
supervised learning	A fundamental form of learning in which the cerebellar circuitry automatically reduces errors over several trials. A form of procedural learning, also known as trial-and-error learning.
systems thinking	Popularized by Senge. The ability to consider the abstract principles of cause and effect at work over time in organizations. Key ideas are cycles of effects, reinforcing feedback, balancing feedback and delay. Useful for abstract, big picture analyses.
Talent Diversity	The idea that every organization needs - and needs to encourage - a diversity of talents. This generally indicates that the Dyslexia Decathlon set of strengths should be strongly encouraged.
toxic reading failure	A failure to read leading to the creation of mental abscesses that actively interfere with subsequent learning to read.
Unconventional Thinking	The conventional thinking skills are those associated with analytic, step-at-a-time problem solving skills. Unconventional talents are associated with different skills - such as design, 'fuzzy thinking' and intuition. Closely linked to Talent Diversity.
unsupervised learning	A fundamental form of mammalian learning in which, over time, the brain self-organizes itself to recognize the statistical regularities in the input without the need for any explicit training. Also known as statistical learning. A form of procedural learning.
Visual Word Form Area	The region of the temporal lobe associated in general with visual expertise, adapted for immediate recognition of visual words. The necessary neural circuits are developed following several years of practice.
VWFA	Visual Word Form Area
ZPD	Zone of Proximal Development
Zone of Proximal Development	A Vygotskian concept, referring to the boundaries of a child's knowledge. The ZPD is the region - for a given concept - where a child can make progress with adult support but will not make the progress unaided.

References

1. Nicolson, R.I., *Positive Dyslexia: Working to our Strengths*, in *IDA Parents Conference*2012: Baltimore MD.

2. Nicolson, R.I. and A.S. Agahi, *Positive Dyslexia*, in *BDA Handbook*, A.J. Fawcett and K. Saunders, Editors. 2013, British Dyslexia Association: Bracknell. p. 26-29.

3. Miles, T.R., *Dyslexia: the pattern of difficulties*. 1993, London: Whurr.

4. World Federation of Neurology, *Report of research group on dyslexia and world illiteracy*. 1968, Dallas: WFN.

5. Shaywitz, S.E., *Current concepts - Dyslexia*. New England Journal of Medicine, 1998. **338**: p. 307-312.

6. Siegel, L.S., *Why we do not need intelligence test scores in the definition and analyses of Learning Disabilities*. Journal of Learning Disabilities, 1989. **22**: p. 514-518.

7. Shaywitz, S., *Dyslexia*. Scientific American, 1996(November): p. 78-84.

8. Hubbell, H.V., *Dyslexia the Movie*, 2012.

9. IDA, *Definition of Dyslexia (Fact Sheet)*, 2002, International Dyslexia Association: Baltimore, MD.

10. Nicolson, R.I., *The Dyslexia Ecosystem*. Dyslexia: An International Journal of Research and Practice, 2002. **8**: p. 55-66.

11. Seligman, M.E.P., *Authentic happiness: Using the new positive psychology to realize your potential for lasting fulfilment*. 2002, New York: Free Press.

12. Geschwind, N., *Why Orton was right*. Annals of Dyslexia, 1982. **32**: p. 13-30.

13. Winkler, H., L. Oliver, and N. Baines, *Hank Zipzer 1: The World's Greatest Underachiever and the Crazy Classroom Cascade* 2011, London: Walker Books.

14. Stewart, J., *Winning is not enough: The autobiography*. 2010, London: Headline Book Publishing.

15. Schmiedek, F., M. Lovden, and U. Lindenberger, *Younger Adults Show Long-Term Effects of Cognitive Training on Broad Cognitive Abilities Over 2 Years*. Developmental Psychology, 2014. **50**(9): p. 2304-2310.

16. Schultz, P., *Failure*. 2007, Orlando FL: Harcourt.

17. Laws, J.M., *The Laws Field Guide to the Sierra Nevada*. 2007, Berkeley CA: Heyday Books.

18. West, T.G., *In the Mind's Eye: Creative Visual Thinkers, Gifted Dyslexics and the rise of visual technologies*. 2nd ed. 2009, Amherst, NY: Prometheus Books.

19. West, T.G., *In the Mind's Eye: Visual thinkers, gifted people with learning difficulties, computer images, and the ironies of creativity*. 1991, Buffalo NY: Prometheus Books.

20. West, T.G., *Thinking Like Einstein: Returning to Our Visual Roots with the Emerging Revolution in Computer Information Visualisation*. 2004, New York: Prometheus Books.

21. Vail, P.L., *Gifts, talents, and the dyslexias: Wellsprings, springboards, and finding Foley's rocks*. Annals of Dyslexia 1990. **40**: p. 3-17.

22. Davis, R.D. and E.M. Braun, *The Gift of Dyslexia: Why Some of the Brightest People Can't Read and How They Can Learn*. 1997, London: Souvenir Press.

23. Eide, B.L. and F.F. Eide, *The Dyslexic Advantage: Unlocking the Hidden Potential of the Dyslexic Brain.* 2011, London: Hay House.

24. Agahi, A.S., P.P. Sepulveda, and R.I. Nicolson, *Careers, Talents and Dyslexia: Working to one's strengths.* Dyslexia, 2015, submitted.

25. Mumford, S.R. and R.I. Nicolson, *Dyslexia and Intelligence: Positive evidence on the discrepancy.* Dyslexia, 2014, submitted.

26. Adey, P., M. Shayer, and C. Yates, *Thinking Science: The Materials of the CASE Project.* 2001, Cheltenham: Nelson Thornes Ltd.

27. Shayer, M. and D. Ginsburg, *Thirty years on - a large anti-Flynn effect? (II): 13-and 14-year-olds. Piagetian tests of formal operations norms 1976-2006/7.* British Journal of Educational Psychology, 2009. **79**: p. 409-418.

28. Nicolson, R.I. and A.J. Fawcett, *Dyslexia, Learning and the Brain.* 2008, Boston: MIT Press.

29. Wolf, M. and P.G. Bowers, *The double-deficit hypothesis for the developmental dyslexias.* Journal of Educational Psychology, 1999. **91**: p. 415-438.

30. Goswami, U., *Why theories about developmental dyslexia require developmental designs.* Trends in Cognitive Sciences, 2003. **7**(12): p. 534-540.

31. Facoetti, A., et al., *The role of visuospatial attention in developmental dyslexia: evidence from a rehabilitation study.* Cognitive Brain Research, 2003. **15**(2): p. 154-164.

32. Blau, V., et al., *Reduced Neural Integration of Letters and Speech Sounds Links Phonological and Reading Deficits in Adult Dyslexia (vol 19, pg 503, 2009).* Current Biology, 2009. **19**(12): p. 1064-1064.

33. Nicolson, R.I. and A.J. Fawcett, *Automaticity: A new framework for dyslexia research?* Cognition, 1990. **35**(2): p. 159-182.

34. Tallal, P., S. Miller, and R.H. Fitch, *Neurobiological basis of speech - a case for the pre-eminence of temporal processing.* Annals of the New York Academy of Sciences, 1993. **682**: p. 27-47.

35. Nicolson, R.I. and A.J. Fawcett, *Procedural learning difficulties: reuniting the developmental disorders?* Trends in Neurosciences, 2007. **30**(4): p. 135-141.

36. Stein, J.F. and V. Walsh, *To see but not to read; The magnocellular theory of dyslexia.* Trends in Neurosciences, 1997. **20**: p. 147-152.

37. Galaburda, A.M., *The testosterone hypothesis: Assessment since Geschwind and Behan (1982).* Annals of Dyslexia, 1990. **40**: p. 18-38.

38. Nicolson, R.I., A.J. Fawcett, and P. Dean, *Developmental dyslexia: the cerebellar deficit hypothesis.* Trends in Neurosciences, 2001. **24**(9): p. 508-511.

39. Lundberg, I., A. Olofsson, and S. Wall, *Reading and Spelling skills in the First School Years predicted fron phonetic awareness skills in Kindergarten.* Scandinavian Journal of Psychology, 1980. **21**: p. 159-173.

40. Bradley, L. and P.E. Bryant, *Difficulties in auditory organisation as a possible cause of reading backwardness.* Nature, 1978. **271**: p. 746-747.

41. Vellutino, F.R., *Dyslexia: Theory and research.* 1979, Cambridge, MA: MIT Press.

42. Stanovich, K.E., *Explaining the Differences between the Dyslexic and the Garden-Variety Poor Reader: The Phonological-Core Variable-Difference Model.* Journal of Learning Disabilities, 1988. **21**(10): p. 590-604.

43. Yeatman, J.D., et al., *Development of white matter and reading skills.* Proceedings of the National Academy of Sciences of the United States of America, 2012. **109**(44): p. E3045-E3053.

44. Fawcett, A.J. and R.I. Nicolson, *Automatisation deficits in balance for dyslexic children.* Perceptual and Motor Skills, 1992. **75**(2): p. 507-529.

45. Nicolson, R.I. and A.J. Fawcett, *Long-term learning in dyslexic children.* European Journal of Cognitive Psychology, 2000. **12**: p. 357-393.

46. Leiner, H.C., A.L. Leiner, and R.S. Dow, *Reappraising the cerebellum: what does the hindbrain contribute to the forebrain.* Behavioural Neuroscience, 1989. **103**: p. 998-1008.

47. Desmond, J.E. and J.A. Fiez, *Neuroimaging studies of the cerebellum: language, learning and memory.* Trends in Cognitive Sciences, 1998. **2**(9): p. 355-362.

48. Doya, K., *What are the computations of the cerebellum, the basal ganglia and the cerebral cortex?* Neural Networks, 1999. **12**(7-8): p. 961-974.

49. Ullman, M.T., *Contributions of memory circuits to language: the declarative/procedural model.* Cognition, 2004. **92**(1-2): p. 231-270.

50. Kuhl, P.K., *Early language acquisition: Cracking the speech code.* Nature Reviews Neuroscience, 2004. **5**(11): p. 831-843.

51. Westermann, G., et al., *Neuroconstructivism.* Developmental Science, 2007. **10**(1): p. 75-83.

52. Karmiloff-Smith, A., *Development itself is the key to understanding developmental disorders.* Trends in Cognitive Sciences, 1998. **2**(10): p. 389-398.

53. Goswami, U., *Sensorimotor impairments in dyslexia: getting the beat.* Developmental Science, 2006. **9**(3): p. 257-259.

54. Froyen, D.J.W., G. Willems, and L. Blomert, *Evidence for a specific cross-modal association deficit in dyslexia: an electrophysiological study of letter speech sound processing.* Developmental Science, 2011. **14**(4): p. 635-648.

55. Bosse, M.L., M.J. Tainturier, and S. Valdois, *Developmental dyslexia: The visual attention span deficit hypothesis.* Cognition, 2007. **104**(2): p. 198-230.

56. Galaburda, A.M., *The Testosterone Hypothesis - Assessment since Geschwind and Behan, 1982.* Annals of Dyslexia, 1990. **40**: p. 18-38.

57. Lum, J.A.G., M.T. Ullman, and G. Conti-Ramsden, *Procedural learning is impaired in dyslexia: Evidence from a meta-analysis of serial reaction time studies.* Research in Developmental Disabilities, 2013. **34**(10): p. 3460-3476.

58. Guttorm, T.K., et al., *Newborn Event-Related Potentials Predict Poorer Pre-Reading Skills in Children at Risk for Dyslexia.* Journal of Learning Disabilities, 2010. **43**(5): p. 391-401.

59. McPhillips, M., P.G. Hepper, and G. Mulhern, *Effects of replicating primary-reflex movements on specific reading difficulties in children: a randomised, double-blind, controlled trial.* Lancet, 2000. **355**(9203): p. 537-541.

60. Lyytinen, H., et al., *Psychophysiology of developmental dyslexia: a review of findings including studies of children at risk for dyslexia.* Journal of Neurolinguistics, 2005. **18**(2): p. 167-195.

61. Hewitt-Main, J., *Dyslexia behind Bars: Final report of a pioneering teaching and mentoring project at Chelmsford Pridon - 4 yearson*, 2012: Benfleet, Essex.

62. Holt, J., *How Children Fail.* 1964, New York: Pitman.

63. Maloney, E.A., *Math anxiety: who has it, why it develops, and how to guard against it (vol 16, pg 404, 2012).* Trends in Cognitive Sciences, 2012. **16**(10): p. 526-526.

64. Young, C.B., S.S. Wu, and V. Menon, *The Neurodevelopmental Basis of Math Anxiety.* Psychological Science, 2012. **23**(5): p. 492-501.

65. Goetz, T., et al., *Do Girls Really Experience More Anxiety in Mathematics?* Psychological Science, 2013. **24**(10): p. 2079-2087.

66. Lyons, I.M. and S.L. Beilock, *When Math Hurts: Math Anxiety Predicts Pain Network Activation in Anticipation of Doing Math.* Plos One, 2012. **7**(10).

67. Maier, S.F. and M.E.P. Seligman, *Learned Helplessness - Theory and Evidence.* Journal of Experimental Psychology-General, 1976. **105**(1): p. 3-46.

68. Schwabe, L. and O.T. Wolf, *Stress and multiple memory systems: from 'thinking' to 'doing'.* Trends in Cognitive Sciences, 2013. **17**(2): p. 60-68.

69. Abramson, L.Y., M.E.P. Seligman, and J.D. Teasdale, *Learned Helplessness in Humans - Critique and Reformulation.* Journal of Abnormal Psychology, 1978. **87**(1): p. 49-74.

70. Tian, Y., et al., *Exploring the system-wide costs of falls in older people in Torbay*, 2013.

71. Meltzoff, A.N., et al., *Foundations for a New Science of Learning.* Science, 2009. **325**(5938): p. 284-288.

72. Garcia-Sierra, A., et al., *Bilingual language learning: An ERP study relating early brain responses to speech, language input, and later word production.* Journal of Phonetics, 2011. **39**(4): p. 546-557.

73. Poulin-Dubois, D., et al., *The effects of bilingualism on toddlers' executive functioning.* Journal of Experimental Child Psychology, 2011. **108**(3): p. 567-579.

74. Morales, J., A. Calvo, and E. Bialystok, *Working memory development in monolingual and bilingual children.* Journal of Experimental Child Psychology, 2013. **114**(2): p. 187-202.

75. Greenberg, A., B. Bellana, and E. Bialystok, *Perspective-taking ability in bilingual children: Extending advantages in executive control to spatial reasoning.* Cognitive Development, 2013. **28**(1): p. 41-50.

76. Bialystok, E., F.I.M. Craik, and G. Luk, *Bilingualism: consequences for mind and brain.* Trends in Cognitive Sciences, 2012. **16**(4): p. 240-250.

77. Meltzoff, A.N. and M.K. Moore, *Imitation of facial and manual gestures by human neonates.* Science, 1977. **198**: p. 75-78.

78. Hebb, D.O., *The organization of behavior.* 1949, New York: Wiley.

79. Montessori, M., *The Montessori Method.* 1912/2008, Blacksburg VA: EarthAngel Books.

80. Inhelder, B. and J. Piaget, *The Growth of Logical Thinking from Childhood to Adolescence.* 1958, New York: Basic Books.

81. Vygotsky, L., *Thought and Language.* 1986, Cambridge MA: MIT Press.

82. Feuerstein, R., R.S. Feuerstein, and L.H. Falk, *Beyond Smarter: Mediated Learning and the Brain's Capacity for Change.* 2010, New York: Teachers College Press.

83. Feuerstein, R., et al., *Instrumental enrichment: An intervention program for cognitive modifiability.* 1980, Baltimore MD: University Park Press.

84. Frith, U., *A developmental framework for developmental dyslexia.* Annals of dyslexia, 1986. **36**(1): p. 67-81.

85. Orton, J.L., *The Orton-Gillingham approach*, in *The disabled reader: Education of the dyslexic child*, J. Money, Editor. 1966, Johns Hopkins Press: Baltimore.

86. Seligman, M.E.P., *Learned optimism.* Second ed. 2006, New York: Pocket Books.

87. Papert, S., *Mindstorms: Children, computers and powerful ideas.* 1980, New York: Basic Books.

88. NICHD, *Report of the National Reading Panel: Teaching children to read.* 2000, Washington DC: National Institute for Child Health and Human Development.

89. Stuebing, K.K., et al., *A response to recent reanalyses of the National Reading Panel report: Effects of systematic phonics instruction are practically significant.* Journal of Educational Psychology, 2008. **100**(1): p. 123-134.

90. Stanovich, K.E., *Matthew effects in reading: Some consequences of individual differences in the acquisition of literacy.* Reading Research Quarterly, 1986. **21**: p. 360-407.

91. Nicolson, R., A. Fawcett, and M. Nicolson, *Evaluation of a computer-based reading intervention in infant and junior schools.* Journal of Research in Reading, 2000. **23**(2): p. 194 - 209.

92. Regtvoort, A., H. Zijlstra, and A. van der Leij, *The Effectiveness of a 2-year Supplementary Tutor-assisted Computerized Intervention on the Reading Development of Beginning Readers at Risk for Reading Difficulties: A Randomized Controlled Trial.* Dyslexia, 2013. **19**(4): p. 256-280.

93. Saine, N.L., et al., *Computer-Assisted Remedial Reading Intervention for School Beginners at Risk for Reading Disability.* Child Development, 2011. **82**(3): p. 1013-1028.

94. Franceschini, S., et al., *Action Video Games Make Dyslexic Children Read Better.* Current Biology, 2013. **23**(6): p. 462-466.

95. Hillman, C.H., K.I. Erickson, and A.F. Kramer, *Be smart, exercise your heart: exercise effects on brain and cognition.* Nature Reviews Neuroscience, 2008. **9**(1): p. 58-65.

96. Knowles, M.S., F.H. Elwood, and R.A. Swanson, *The Adult Learner.* 7th ed. 2011, Oxford: Butterworth-Heinemann.

97. Niemann, C., B. Godde, and C. Voelcker-Rehage, *Not only cardiovascular, but also coordinative exercise increases hippocampal volume in older adults.* Frontiers in aging neuroscience, 2014. **6**: p. 170-170.

98. Burciu, R.G., et al., *Brain Changes Associated with Postural Training in Patients with Cerebellar Degeneration: A Voxel-Based Morphometry Study.* Journal of Neuroscience, 2013. **33**(10): p. 4594-4604.

99. Mayne, B., *Goal Mapping: How to Turn Your Dreams into Realities.* 2006, London: Watkins Publishing Ltd.

100. Gerber, P.J., R. Ginsberg, and H.B. Reiff, *Identifying Alterable Patterns in Employment Success for Highly Successful Adults with Learning-Disabilities.* Journal of Learning Disabilities, 1992. **25**(8): p. 475-487.

101. Raskind, M.H., et al., *Patterns of change and predictors of success in individuals with learning disabilities: Results from a twenty-year longitudinal study.* Learning Disabilities Research and Practice, 1999. **14**(1): p. 35-49.

102. Goldberg, R.J., et al., *Predictors of Success in Individuals with Learning Disabilities: A Qualitative Analysis of a 20-Year Longitudinal Study*. Learning Disabilities Research & Practice, 2003. **18**(4): p. 222–236.

103. Wolff, U., *Artistic Talents and Dyslexia: A Genuine Connection?*, in *Dyslexia and Creativity: Investigations from Differing Perspectives*. 2010. p. 67-78.

104. Logan, J., *Dyslexic Entrepreneurs: The Incidence; Their Coping Strategies and Their Business Skills*. Dyslexia, 2009. **15**(4): p. 328-346.

105. Holland, J.L., *Dictionary of Holland Occupational Codes*. 1996: Psychological Assessment Resources.

106. Lantz, C., *Psychology Student Employability Guide*. 2008, York UK: Higher Education Academy Psychology Network.

107. Rath, T., *Strengths Finder 2.0*. 2007, New York: Gallup.

108. Pink, D.H., *A Whole New Mind: Why Right-Brainers Will Rule the Future*. 2005, New York: Penguin Books.

109. Agahi, A.S. and R.I. Nicolson, *Work strengths of dyslexic students: A comparative study*. Dyslexia, in preparation, 2014, in preparation.

110. Achor, S., *The Happiness Advantage*. 2010, New York: Crown Publishing Group.

111. Kimsey-House, H., et al., *Co-Active Coaching: Changing Business, Transforming Lives*. 2011, Boston: Nicholas Brealey.

112. Jones, A., *Winning at Interview: A new way to succeed*. 2000, New York: Random House.

113. Watkins, M., *The First 90 Days: Critical success strategies for new leaders at all levels*. 2003, Boston MA: Harvard Business School Press Ltd.

114. Mumford, T.V., et al., *The Team Role Test: Development and validation of a team role knowledge situational judgment test*. Journal of Applied Psychology, 2008. **93**(2): p. 250-267.

115. Wrzesniewski, A., J.M. Berg, and J.E. Dutton, *Turn the job you have into the job you want*. Harvard Business Review, 2010(Jun 2010): p. 114-117.

116. Rackham, N., *SPIN Selling*. 1995: Gower Publishing Ltd, Farnham, UK.

117. Feigenbaum, E. and P. McCorduck, *The Fifth Generation: Japan's challenge to the world*. 1984, London: Pan Books.

118. Sainsbury, D., *The Race to the Top: A Review of Government's Science and Innovation Policies*, Treasury, Editor 2007, HMSO: London.

119. Senge, P.M., *The Fifth Discipline: The Art and Practice of the Learning Organization*. 1993, Castle Rock, CO: Century Books.

120. Covey, S.R., *The Seven Habits of Highly Effective People*. 1989, London: Simon & Schuster.

121. Kaplan, R.S. and D.P. Norton, *The Balanced Scorecard: measures that drive performance*. Harvard Business Review, 1992(Jan-Feb): p. 61-66.

122. Kaplan, R.S. and D.P. Norton, *Strategy Maps: Converting intangible assets into tangible outcomes*. 2004, Boston, MA: Harvad Business School Press.

123. Porter, M.E. and M.R. Kramer, *Creating Shared Value: How to reinvent capitalism - and unleash a wave of innovation and growth*. Harvard Business Review, 2011(Jan-Feb 2011): p. 1-17.

124.   Ancona,   D.,   "Leadership   in   an   Age   of   Uncertainty"   2005, http://mitleadership.mit.edu/pdf/LeadershipinanAgeofUncertainty-researchbrief.pdf *Leadership in an Age of Uncertainty*. 2005.

125.   Ruyle, K.E. and J.E. Orr, *Fundamentals of Competency Modeling*, in *Talent Management Handbook (2nd Ed): Creating a sustainable competitive advantage by selecting,developing and promoting the best people* L.A. Berger and D.R. Berger, Editors. 2011, McGraw Hill: New York. p. 22-32.

126.   Butler, R.F., *Creating Competitive Advantage through Cultural Dexterity*, in *Talent Management Handbook (2nd Ed): Creating a sustainable competitive advantage by selecting,developing and promoting the best people* L.A. Berger and D.R. Berger, Editors. 2011, McGraw Hill: New York.

127.   Bruner, J., *The process of education*. 1960, Cambridge MA: Harvard University Press.

Index

Printed in Great Britain
by Amazon

79909219R00100